EFFRIES

RADIO DOTUN

for... YOU KNOW WHO

www.effries.co.uk

EFFRIES
RADIO DOTUN
Edited by Beatrice Steele
© 2023 dotun adebayo
Published by The X Press: xpressbooks@hotmail.com
www.effries.co.uk
A catalogue version is available at The British Library
ISBN-13: 9781902934587
Printed and bound by CPI Group (UK) Ltd, Croydon, CR0 4YY

EFFRIES is made possible by the generous support of the following:

CHRISTOPHER HAYWARD

VIV BROUGHTON
ANDREW RICHES
HELEN KINGSBURY
GUNILLA KARLBORG
JEREMY WALKER
SIMON GRAHAM
HELEN AULD
DANIEL OLUYOMI
CHRISTINE OLUFUNMILAYO OLUYOMI-ADEBAYO
PAUL VINOGRADOFF
GLORIA ABRAMOFF
CHRISTOPHER WIELAND
MOJISOLA ADEBAYO
DIRAN ADEBAYO
LEO HAIDER & FAMILY
DAVID HALL

MATS BÄCKER, MATTHEW SEMISCH, BOBBY JOSEPH, ANDREW
MALONE, LELA KOGBARA, JAMIE ROBUS, JOANNE WALTERS,
CARLA BATTISTI, MARK ARNOLD, THOMAS JACKSON, EDDIE
PITMAN, TOM LONGFIELD, PAUL WATERS, ROBERT MARRETT,
DAVID BURDEN, SAM ROBINSON, PETER COMPTON,
SEAN FARRINGTON, PHIL BUNCE, SEB CHESIRE, KATE HAYES,
WINSOME CORNISH, DAN NELSON, TOM MILLINGTON

Thank you all from the bottom of my heart.
Dotun Adebayo, SEPTEMBER 2023

EFFRIES

IN THE GLOOMY SILENCE, DEEP IN THE COCKPIT OF YOUR HEART IS THE YOU YOU'RE RUNNING FROM.

JOOKS, YOU BUMBOCLAAT, HAPPY DEAD DAY. WATCH NO FACE, SHITFACE. NOWHERE TO RUN, NOWHERE TO HIDE. I'M MAKING DUPPY. MAY GOD HAVE MERCY ON YOUR BATTYHOLE. MIDNIGHT, YEAH? YOU KNOW WHO.

Shitface. Happy dead day. Making duppy. I'm shitting myself. I mean, how did I get myself in this mess in the first place and what kind of a woman would leave a message like that on my phone? I don't know what I'm supposed to have done. Someone tried to run me down just last week. Then tried to shoot me. I'm really shitting myself. I've got to know who. I've got to know why. By midnight.

YOU KNOW WHO. YOU KNOW WHY. YOU KNOW WHAT. YOU JUST CAN'T FACE IT. IT'S COMPLEX. LIKE OEDIPUS.

Someone's trying to kill me and you're talking bollocks. I keep saying I never saw my parents having it off.

IN THE NAME OF THE FATHER THE SON AND THE HOLY GHOST YOU DEFINITELY DID. WITHOUT A SHADOW OF A DOUBT. YOU DON'T REMEMBER? TOO YOUNG. BEDSIT FAMILY AND ALL. YOU COULDN'T AVOID BEING A WITNESS.

It never happened. I swear. Not even in the womb. It never happened. And I wasn't molested by my teachers neither.

COURSE YOU WERE. BOYS SCHOOL. IN THOSE DAYS. ALL THOSE KIDDY FIDDLERS. LOCKED IN THE HEADMASTER'S STUDY. SIX OF THE BEST. UP THE ARSENAL.

What's that got to do with anything?

DO YOU BELIEVE IN KARMA? ONLY YOU CAN ANSWER.

Well, yeah, I guess. How would I know?

EFFRIES

NOTHING IS BRIGHT AND BEAUTIFUL WHEN YOU LOSE YOUR VIRGINITY – SORRY, I MEAN HUMANITY.

What's that supposed to mean?

YOU MUST HAVE DONE SOMETHING FOR SOMEONE TO TRY TO KILL YOU. DID YOU CHEAT? HONESTLY, YOU AND YOUR DICK.

Don't be a prick. I'm a national treasure.

ARE THOSE NOT YOUR PRINTS ALL OVER THIS? NOT TO TALK OF YOUR ATOMIC DNA. WHEN THE TECHNOLOGY IS INVENTED – ANY DAY NOW – IT WILL NOT ONLY PUT YOU AT THE SCENE BUT AT THE MOMENT OF THE CRIME. IT WILL BE THE END OF THE ALIBI AS WE KNOW IT.

It's not like I'm Cinderella. Tried to run me down like I'm some piece of shit with ugly sisters.

NOT TO TALK OF THE END OF ADULTERY. FAR MORE COMMON WHERE THE CLIMATE'S SULTRY.

Do you know who I am?

YOU ARE A PERPETUAL STATE OF THE NILE.

I'm lucky to be alive. If my fairy godmother hadn't come out the sky and plucked me up I'd be deadmeat, the eyewitness says. She says it was all my fault. I wasn't looking where I was going, when the car 'lost control' and headed for me top speed. I didn't even see who.

I MEAN 'DENIAL'.

And then the dog next door dies in my arms. Came in through the hole in the garden wall as usual. I grabbed it by the collar to shoo it back out and then *POP*. Fucking *POP* and it was gone.

IN DENIAL.

EFFRIES

When I saw the trickle of blood from the hole between its eyes I realised I had dodged a bullet. Lucky to be alive. But I can't tell anybody. Definitely not the police. They would want to know why. Why someone's trying to run me down. I don't know but I can't say I don't know, can I? You know what ol' bill's like, they'll never believe me. I can't tell my neighbours neither. They're putting up reward posters for Rover's return. I can't tell them that they're wasting their time. How will I explain that the bullet was meant for me?

I won't miss again.

DID YOU MENTION THE WIFE AND KIDS? IS THAT WHY SHE'S GOING TO KILL YOU?

That's what's so crazy about this, I'm not like the others. Not since my accident. I'm not who I used to be. Monogamy used to be a mass of confusion but I totally get it now.

KARMA IS A MOTHERFUCKER. NO SENSE GIVING IT THE OLD *IT WASN'T ME, IT'S A MIX-UP, IT MUST BE SOME OTHER ME.* THE JUDGE AIN'T GOING TO BUY THAT. AS FAR AS SHE'S CONCERNED YOU ARE YOU.

Screw the judge. Someone's murdering me. I need to know who and I need to know why. I've got to get to the bottom of this.

THERE'S NOBODY BETTER THAN ME AT GETTING TO THE BOTTOM. I USED TO BE A PRIEST, REMEMBER? IF I CAN'T TELL YOU WHO IS TRYING TO KILL YOU AND WHY, NOBODY CAN. THE ANSWER ALWAYS LIES IN THE PAST. THAT'S WHERE YOU'LL FIND THE MESS YOU'VE GOT YOURSELF IN. I'LL TAKE YOU THERE IF YOU ARE ABSOLUTELY SURE. COS THERE AIN'T NO TURNING BLACK WHEN YOU GO DOWN THAT PARTICULAR BANANA BOTTOM.

Just do your thing. Please. Do your thing. Whatever it takes. If that's the only way of finding out who is trying to 'X' me, beam me down Scotty. Let's go living in the past. IT DON'T WORK LIKE THAT. THIS AIN'T BACK TO THE

FUTURE. YOU CAN'T SIMPLY GO BACK TO THE PAST. YOU KNOW WHAT THEY SAY, IF MUHAMMAD CAN'T COME TO THE MOUNTAIN IN THE NAME OF OUR LORD JESUS CHRIST, THE PAST CAN COME TO YOU.

Bring me, bruv, bring me. Do what you got to do. I just got to stop shitting myself, looking over my shoulder, wondering what's next. I dare not leave my yard before midnight. I'm so para I don't trust no one. Especially not you. Do what you gotta do.

OKAY, IF YOU'RE ABSOLUTELY SURE, LOOK IN MY EYES. YOU SEE MY PUPILS SPINNING ROUND? SEE IF YOU CAN FOLLOW. ROUND AND ROUND AND ROUND AND ROUND. TOO FAST, OH, OKAY, I'LL SLOW DOWN. AND... NOW... I'LL SPIN THEM THE OTHER WAY. AH, THAT'S BETTER. DO YOU FEEL THAT CALM? THAT'S HOW IT'S GOING TO BE AS YOUR EYELIDS GET HEAVIER AND HEAVIER AND HEAVIER. AND... THEY... BEGIN TO CLOSE. AND *SNAP!* YOU'RE BACK TO REALITY. GOOD TIMES. BAD TIMES. HAPPY TIMES AND SAD TIMES. THE YEARS OF YOUR LIFE. TOGETHER. FOR THE FIRST TIME EVER. IN ONE ROOM. ON A ZOOM. SEE WHAT LIGHT THEY SHED. THE THINGS TO BE SAID OR LEFT UNSAID. I KNOW, I KNOW. I KNOW YOU'RE THINKING, IF ONLY WE COULD LAUGH AGAIN AND DANCE AGAIN AND BE BACK WHERE WE WERE AND WHO WE WERE AGAIN, BUT THAT'S IMPOSSIBLE. IT'S NOT, YOU KNOW. FAITH CAN MOVE MOUNTAINS. ANYTHING IS POSSIBLE. EVERYTHING. SOMEONE'S TRYING TO KILL YOU. THE WHAT, THE WHO, THE WHEN AND WHERE, NOT TO TALK OF THE WHY, ARE IN THAT DARK RECESS OF YOUR MIND WHERE YOUR PAST HIDES. SEEK AND YOU SHALL FIND. MIDNIGHT, YEAH?

EFFRIES
FIRST LOAD

The Master of the Household
Has received Her Majesty's command to invite
Mr Jooks Kamiolakamioluwalajoko
To a reception to be given at Buckingham Palace by the Queen

FORTY-TWO
I thought there must be some mistake.

EIGHT
The more you eat
The more you fart

FORTY-TWO
It's gotta be some kind of cock-up. Street kids from Totty don't get to go to the palace to meet the Queen. Especially when they're wanted for murder. And then I thought it must be a trap. I wouldn't put it past them. The cops must know there's no way a kid from the N17s is turning down an invite from the Queen. Even if it means going jail. But what if it's not a trap? What if it's not a mistake? What if this is my lucky day? What if this was meant to be? Me and the Queen, a golden opportunity to get the cops off my back. Mistake or no mistake I'll tell her, tell her straight, that I had nothing to do with the shooting of that copper in east London. I ain't going HMP for a murder I didn't commit. Not with the Queen by my side. Ya get me? So here I am, original young, gifted and black, past the gate-keepers and the Guards, striding across the pink gravel courtyard at the front when I hear some yank tourist cry out.
How come he gets to go through the pearly gates?
I half-turn towards him with a grin. Yeah, things done changed. No more 'No Blacks/No Irish'. It's all lords, ladies and gentlemen now. Bumper to bumper. Bentleys and Rollers.

TWELVE
Bunk me in, will ya? Dominic The Mechanic will give me a tenner for one of them Rollers.

FORTY-TWO
Mate, keep that shit shut. I ain't you no more. You ain't me.
You wanna see how many of this lot have had their Rollers
nicked. Buckingham Palace for fucksake. Ain't no joke.

TWENTY-THREE
You're in the right place if you're on the run. They'll never
think of looking for you here.

FORTY-TWO
Shhhhh! You-know-who has just walked in.

SEVENTEEN
God save you, my grace. All crimes are paid.

EIGHT
Ee-aye-addi-o
God save the Queen

FORTY-TWO
Just like the old Trinny said she would.
How's the wife and kids?
I swear. No word of a lie. I'm standing right next to him all
casual, styling it out like meeting the Queen is no biggie,
like I'm some movie star in and out of palaces on a regular.
Meanwhile I'm shitting myself. It's THE QUEEN. She's no
mug. She'll sniff me out and suss straight away that I'm
a road man who must have bunked in cos road man ain't
supposed to be here. Just like this old Trinny. As it turns
out he is supposed to be here. A moment or two ago he
was telling likely tales of HRHs. I mean really tall tales
like he's played with his steelband at the palace for Her
Majesty six times and at Highgrove for Prince Charles five
times. And how much the royal family love calypso and
how he wouldn't be surprised if they had a little black in
'em. I stood there thinking at least I'm not the only fraud
in here. Like I said, street kids from Totty don't get invited
to the palace. Nor do steel pan players from Port of Spain.
No way. No how. And yet here she is, coming through the
same ornate double doors my man said she would and she

goes right up to him and starts chatting like him and her are spars, while her lady-in-waiting asks me where I'm from. *No, REALLY from.* It don't make no sense.

FORTY
Make it make sense or else it's nonsense. This whole story.

EIGHT
Catch a nigger by the toe...

FORTY-TWO
No word of a lie. Her Majesty's liming with the Trinny, giving it the old 'tally me banana' and Gary Wilmot, you know, the joker... Oh you don't? Not at all? TWENTY, you remember him. New Faces. Mate, you're on mute.

TWENTY-TWENTY
Sorry, I was on mute. Still trying to work this zoom thingy out.

EIGHT
If he hollers let him go.

NINE
Someone's let off a stinker? *Euurrgh!*

TEN
Smelt it dealt it.

FIFTY-NINE
FYI kids, this is a zoom room. You can't smell each other's farts.

TEN
See, your nose is too near your arse.

NINE
Fuck you too.

FIFTY-NINE
Oi! Language

FORTY-TWO

Turns out the joker's a palace regular and knows where to put his cheeky-chappy dimples between me and Her Majesty to make the morning papers. But the Queen doesn't want to talk to him. She wants to talk to me, see. So she gives the joker the elbow and one of the courtiers beside her goes:

Ma'am, may I present Mr K-K-K...

Mr Kamiolakamioluwalajoko, how do you do? What do you do?

What do you do when the Queen asks what do you do? What am I supposed to say? I mean, she's the Queen, you can't lie to her can you? I mean, you just can't. But at the same time you can't stand there and tell her to her face that you're on the run, hiding in plain view, Britain's most wanted, Scotland yardie and all that. As seen on the telly. Seeing my moment of greatness flicker away in HRH's eyes triggered my hay fever. You know what that's like, once I started I couldn't stop sneezing and I had to turn my back on her.

TEN

You turned your back on Her Majesty? You're not allowed.

TWENTY-NINE

Is this a wind-up? You're on the run. And you turn your back on the Queen. You may as well bring back hanging.

FORTY-TWO

It's a miscarriage of justice. They were THIRTY-FOUR's bullets. He should be doing the running. Not me. I'm knackered.

THIRTY-NINE

Those bullets, I remember them. That was some PR stunt.

THIRTY-FOUR

The best. The very best.

THIRTY-NINE

Thought all that was done and dusted years ago. How come ol' bill's still after you?

FORTY-TWO
They want to bring me in guilty like I shot the sheriff. One of the bullets you used to promote Cop Killer all those years ago ends up being used in a cop killing in east London the other day. Chances of that, eh? You're not around so they're coming after me.

NINE
Wow. How much is the reward? Can I have one of them bullets?

THIRTY-FOUR
But this is years later.

FORTY-TWO
Cop died though, you know.

THIRTY-FOUR
Doesn't make me a cop killer.

FORTY-TWO
Yeah, but it was one of your bullets. And if I have to do time for your crime you're a cunt.

EIGHT
Ee-aye-addi-o
You're a fucking cunt

THIRTY-FOUR
How can you be so sure it was one of my nines?

FORTY-TWO
It only takes one to kill a man.

THIRTY-FOUR
Yeah, but you can't prove it was one of mine.

FORTY-TWO
Unproven that it was NOT one of yours either. You know what ol' bill's like, you're guilty until you can prove otherwise.

THIRTY-FOUR
I only sent them out to journalists.

THIRTY-THREE
Fucksake. Journalists? Are you having a laugh?

FORTY-TWO
The cops say I'm as guilty as the bloke who pulled the trigger.

THIRTY-FOUR
That's bollocks.

FORTY-FOUR
What if one of those journalists is the cop killer?

THIRTY-FOUR
No way. That can't happen. No way.

FORTY-FOUR
Cos some of them are unaccounted for. All these years on.
Bullets go AWOL. They go astray. A bullet's only a bullet after all.

THIRTY-FOUR
But my bullets are blanks. They ain't got no gunpowder.

THIRTY-THREE
You're firing blanks? I've heard it all now.

FIFTY-FOUR
Every fool knows a bulletproof way to reinstate gunpowder.

FIFTY-FIVE
Whose bright idea was it to use bullets to promote a book?

FIFTY-EIGHT
People are still talking about it.

THIRTY-THREE
Better than not firing at all, I suppose.

FIFTY-FIVE
It's no laughing matter. Irresponsible. Totally irresponsible.
How could you not consider the unforetold consequences?

THIRTY-FOUR
Consequences? The bullets were legal.

FIFTY-FIVE
That's all you're worried about? A cop's been shot and
killed by one of your bullets and all that concerns you is
whether you can get done for it. It's all me, me, me, me.

FORTY-ONE
Try that nowadays you'll get shot. 9/11. Day the world lost its
virginity. Try that now and, gunpowder or no gunpowder,
they'll bang you up and throw away the keys and that's only
if they run out of ammo for a firing squad. Then there's
your spar the Shoe Bomber.

FORTY-TWO
Didn't spar with him. We lived in a drum. That's all.

SIXTY
No matter. They'll sentence you to forever and take away
your passport and strip you of your citizenship.

FIFTY-SEVEN
You'll have to come home 'cross the Channel in a bathtub.

FIFTY-NINE
You might as well be dead as stateless.

FORTY-TWO
Maybe. But you can't tell the Queen none of that. So when I
eventually stop sneezing, I turn round and she's still there,
somewhat bemused, and I mumble something about being
a publisher. A book publisher. But I think it came out as
'welder'. *A book welder?* Her Majesty asks, enigmatically,
the whole time scrutinising my face like she knows that I
know that she knows I bunked in but she ain't saying.

EIGHT
She's not a fucking grass
She's not a fucking grass
Ee-aye-addi-o
The Queen is not a grass

FORTY-TWO
Cos I'm in the one place in the world where no way some street kid from Totty or a book welder is invited to tea, see.

THIRTY-NINE
You're in Buckingham Palace, having a laugh about book welding with the Queen while you're wanted by ol' bill for murder. You know there's a strait-jacket for that kind of talk.

FORTY-TWO
I know. Insane. But yeah, god's honest truth, it really is the Queen or I'm a black and white minstrel.

TWENTY-TWO
How you bunk in anyhow? That's got to be treason.

FORTY-TWO
That's the joke about it. The Queen says I never bunked in. It's her party. She can invite whoever she wants.

THIRTY-NINE
But you're on the run. Why would she invite you?

FORTY-TWO
Swear to God, I have no idea. Wish I had asked her.

THIRTY
Did somebody say PARTEEE?

THIRTY-ONE
It's a palace party. Not a house party.

THIRTY
Why wasn't I invited?

THIRTY-ONE
Cos you ain't done nothing to make the Queen invite you.

THIRTY
Kings, queens. They're all the frigging same.

NINE
Buckingham Palace. Cor! Are you famous?

FORTY-TWO
No, but I will be.

THIRTY-THREE
When they put up the WANTED poster.

TEN
Wish my teachers could see you now. The head hates me.

FORTY-TWO
What, Ledaker? Headmaster.

TEN
Says I'm a hooligan.

FORTY-TWO
Believe. You're a constant reminder of my one boy crimewave in the N17s. *Your dinner money or my pen knife.*

TEN
You're always blaming me. NINE started it.

NINE
You fucking grass.

TEN
Sticks and stones.

EIGHT
Ee-aye-addi-o
TEN's a fucking grass.

TEN
Takes one to know one, parlez vous
Takes one to know one,
Stick that up your big bum
Inky-pinky parlez vous.

TWENTY-TWENTY
First thing the old man said when I got into uni:
Remember your old head said you would never make university.

TWENTY-SEVEN
He never forgot that. Said the same thing to me an' all when I finally graduated. Ledaker summoned him to Black Boy Lane, to tell the old man how you are nothing but a gangster. When the old man said he expected you to go to Oxford, Ledaker laughed his head off, in the old man's face, like that was the most absurd thing he had ever heard. Like he would personally see to it that you didn't.

FORTIES
Mate, amount of times I've heard that story.

THIRTIES
And every time he tells it the old man's like:
I've never told you this before...

THIRTY-NINE
Really bugged him.

TWENTY-NINE
Pisses him off. To this day. After all these years.

EIGHT
Wogamatter? You *browned off?*

FORTY-TWO
What's with the screw, make your face hurt you.

FIFTEEN
Fuck off. The lot of you.

FORTY-TWO
You wanna watch your mouth, mate, badding up yourself like a prick. Don't get me ignorant.

EIGHT
Go black home and you'll be all white in the morning.

FORTY-TWO
Have some respect. Not having that. None of that. Got a good mind to go back in time and smack you in the teeth.

FIFTEEN
What you gonna do about it? You can't touch me. Wanna fight? I'll knock your block off. You won't know what hit you.

FORTY-TWO
Come on then, tough guy. I'll knock you out.

FIFTY
Fight? Whoa. You can't be talking to your olders like that. You're going to get a slap. What's the matter with you?

FIFTEEN
Look at my hand. It's killing me. The old man. Last night. Whacked the hell out of me. I'm not taking it no more.

FORTY-TWO
Then behave. Stop messing around you miserable git.

FIFTY-FOUR
I have forgotten about it. Look. See? Still broken. After all these years. It's no biggie. You learn to live with it. You're just feeling it a little way different. That's all.

FIFTY-FIVE
Who feels it knows it but it's not like he broke it on purpose. You put your hand in harm's way, yeah? I remember.

TWENTY-TWENTY
Go hospital.

FIFTEEN
And tell them what? My old man broke my hand. Why does he hate me? Why?

FIFTY
He doesn't hate you. He's your dad.

FIFTEEN
So I'm supposed to take this forever? Cos he's my old man.

TWENTY-TWENTY
Go hospital.

FIFTY-SEVEN
What do you expect from being chucked out of school? Messed it up for all of us.

FORTY-TWO
After all we've been through. Do you never think about tomorrow? Do you not think about yesterday?

FIFTEEN
Swear to God, I'll kill him next time. I've got a flick knife now. I'll fucking murder him.

FIFTY-FIVE
See, that's why you got a beating. Maybe you need another. You haven't got time to be killing people. Especially not your old man. Can't you see you're on your own? No teachers. No school. You've got 'O' Levels coming up. Read your frigging books. Every day. Every moment of the day. How hard can that be? Go to the frigging library. All day every day like you're supposed to. Even if all you do is let off stink bombs. Put your heart in it.

FIFTEEN
He's such a dirty fighter. He lost it when he read the letter from school saying I was expelled. What am I supposed to do?

TWENTY-TWENTY
Go hospital.

SIXTY
Yes, go to hospital. Get it seen to. That's my hand too, y'know.

THIRTY-THREE
Not to talk of your bollocks.

THIRTY
No offence, 'nuff slapstick, let's get this shubs popping.

FIFTY-EIGHT
Not everybody is up yet. It's only five past. Give it a couple.

THIRTY-THREE
What do you think this is, BMT?

TWENTY-EIGHT
You sure you can't see me from the waist down on this zoom thingy?

FORTY-FOUR
Black Man Time. Whatever happened to face to face?

FORTY-EIGHT
Face to face done, man. This is the future. Just as well with FIFTEEN and his Swiss army knife roaming around.

FIFTEEN
Piss off. I'll stab you first, cunt, until I can't stab you no more. Then I'll stab you some more.

FORTY-EIGHT
All them little fuckries done. Face to face it. Move on. Reinvention is the mother of invention. Whoever and whatever you want to be. Long as you got the wherewithal.

SIXTEEN
Yeah? What do you mean?

FORTY-EIGHT
All that living on the frontline – that's not me no more.

THIRTIES
So, mister burn baby burn, what is wrong with you? You know you don't do yourself no favours. How the hell you burn down school and think you'll get away with it?

FIFTEEN
What's it got to do with you?

THIRTIES
Everything. You're in my bleeding way. All of us. That was THE BIGGEST FUCK-UP. You get chucked out of school and because of that you're going to fail your 'O' Levels and because of retakes we are going to lose a year of our education which we can never catch up on for the rest of our lives and because we lose a year of our education NINETEEN thinks, sod this, I may as well lose another year bumming around doing nothing. And before we know it, it's two, three, four... seven years behind Fizz and Molly and Ozzie and all them lot in 5F. For the rest of our lives. Six more months. That's all. Six more months and school's done. You're not pulling your bleeding weight. Why couldn't you keep your nose clean for six more months?

FIFTEEN
Sod off, shithead. I tried. Tried my best.

FIFTY-TWO
No sort of good enough.

FORTY
The old man told you to stay in school, smart arse? Didn't he say don't get chucked out? That's all you had to do.

FIFTEEN
I didn't burn down the whole school. Just the chemistry bit. I had to set fire to the exam papers. I came last in the class, see. And there was this Bunsen burner...

EFFRIES

FORTY
You can learn a lot if you use your loaf.

FIFTY
A bit, a lot - whatever - YOU BURNED DOWN THE SCHOOL.

FIFTY-NINE
Okay, calm down, don't get your knickers in a twist.

FIFTY
Why d'you always stick up for him?

FIFTY-NINE
If I don't, who will?

FORTY-EIGHT
You've got to stick up for yourself in this world.

FIFTY
The older I get the more I think this ain't normal. It's bi-polar.

SIXTY
Looks like we're all here. It's that time.

TWENTY-THREE
TWO-TWOs is that really you? Big up yourself. Ages, man, ages. All you TEENS. How long has it been?

THIRTY
Did someone say 'after' PARTEEE?

FIFTY-EIGHT
No time at all. The click of a finger. The blink of an eye. The twirl of a twist like we did last summer. We're no different.

FIFTY
Where is Jooksy? Isn't he doing the honours?

EIGHT
Eeny, Meeny, Miney, mo

EFFRIES

He's a cunt and we all know...

JOOKS
I'm with you. Didn't realise you couldn't see me. Been here
the whole time. Paying attention. Letting you in. Two by
two. Listening. Didn't realise my video was off. Here I am.
Great to see you all, myself, over and over in a wilderness of
mirrors. Amazing. I can hardly believe it. Thanks for coming.
The years of my life. Together. First time ever. Once in a
lifetime. Absolutely brilliant. Modern technology, eh?

NINE
Why d'you keep staring over there, mister? You boss-eyed?

JOOKS
Oh, is this angle better? Cool. Always been a dream of mine,
a fantasy, to bring us all together in one room to talk. Real
talk. Thought it was impossible. Before lockdown none of
us had even heard of zooming. Don't ask me how it works.
Now, why have I brought us all together? Well, I think
about you lot a lot, you know. Who you are. What you are.
How you're living. No doubt you've thought about me too.

NINE
I knew I didn't like you as soon as you opened your gob.
You're nothing like I thought you would be.

JOOKS
I guess none of us is perfect. But we're tight together. One
flesh and blood. Tight. And even though I'm the oldest,
you're all older than me. Mad. Life, eh? It's a hefty sentence.

NINETEEN
Say that again. Size of your chops. How d'you get so fat?

TWENTY-NINE
All that extra timber will do your heart in.

THIRTY
Can we skip the chit-chat and get to the after party.

THIRTY-ONE
Real talk. Should the little'uns even be here? You know what kind of drunken brawls these adult gatherings turn into. If we're getting candid it's no place for kids.

NINE
Who you calling 'little'uns'? Shut your big gob.

JOOKS
For better or worse, I owe you lot. But you lot owe me as well. You have all got a stake in whatever happens to me. See what I mean? If I die young you die young.

FOURTEEN
Live fast die young. Jimmy Dean.

THIRTY-THREE
Fucksake. Get on with it, it'll be Christmas any minute.

JOOKS
Yeah. Course. Mind turning on your video, mate? That little button on the bottom left hand corner. I don't really know what to say. You see, someone's trying to murder me and I'm shitting myself. I really am. She's tried twice already and she's going to have another go at midnight. That's why I'm in hiding. That's why I'm turning to you lot. What's going on? One of you must know what this is about. Which one of you? How did you get myself in this mess? And who is mad enough to pull the trigger or run me over? Who would want to murder you?

NINE
Dead or alive?

THIRTY-THREE
Are you having a laugh? We'll be here all night.

FORTY-NINE
What do you expect when you're king of night-time radio? The amount of people who want to strangle you every time

you sing on air. When that red light comes on anything that comes out your mouth is going to piss somebody off like the house of the rising sun. Goes with the territory.

FIFTY-NINE
You say 'she'. But what about that Brummie who went berserk when he heard you announce over the airwaves that you don't like Asians, and went on that rampage in Handsworth. And even after you appealed for calm and explained on air that it was 'agents' that you don't like – football agents, estate agents, 007 agents, all he could hear was you don't like 'football Asians', 'estate Asians' and '007 Asians' and he went on another rampage in 'little Lagos'.

JOOKS
He was sectioned though, that bloke. He's off the streets.

SIXTY
You sure? You absolutely sure?

JOOKS
Yeah. Until he gets his hearing sorted. No way are they letting him out without letting me know. Not whilst he keeps coming up with new and inventive ways to kill me.

FORTY-FOUR
And he's just one in a million.

JOOKS
What's that supposed to mean?

FIFTY-NINE
You're a marked man.

TWENTY-THREE
You've only got until midnight, you ain't got time.

THIRTY-THREE
Someone's trying to murder you and you don't know why,

yet you're as cool as a cu-koom-ba. Really?

FORTY-THREE
Is this one of them reality TV shows where everybody in a room freaks out?

JOOKS
Tried to run me down. Just last week. Broad daylight. Why?

THIRTY-THREE
No, the you-don't-know-why part.

JOOKS
I haven't a clue. It's got to be meant for you. One of you.

FORTY-TWO
Someone's always trying to run me down. It's the bullets. When you're labelled a cop killer someone always wants to kill you. Even if you're innocent. You know what people are like when they take the law into their own hands. I ain't no cop killer. And the cops know it. But remember the nutter who tried to chuck bleach in my face at Glastonbury? Said she was going to kill me the next time she saw me. I never saw her again but I don't know if she's seen me.

FORTY-NINE
I'm positive it was her who tried to push me in front of that train on the crowded Piccadilly Line platform at Leicester Square. The woman with a teardrop tattoo on her face, remember? I told the cops. Told them what happened. They wouldn't hear it. Particularly when I said who I was. They started accusing me of pushing her under the train.

FIFTY
That'll be why she hasn't tried to murder you since.

FORTY-FOUR
No need to shit yourself then. You have nothing to worry about. Nobody to fear. Your number one suspect is dead.

FIFTY-FOUR

The cops are still going to kick the shit out of you. I'm afraid there's nothing the Queen can do to save you from a bloody good hiding. Ol' bill feel you deserve it. Kicking your head in will give them a great deal of satisfaction.

JOOKS

If not the woman with the teardrop tattoo then who? Who else would have any reason to kill me?

THIRTY-THREE

You asking us or are you talking to yourself?

JOOKS

No, I'm asking you. That's why I'm in this vault. I want to be here to tell the tale after midnight. Whatever it takes.

THIRTY-THREE

What is this mumbo-jumbo? We didn't come here to get dissed.

JOOKS

It is what it is. I carry your heavy load. Imagine, after all these years I'm still trying to touch the tip of my nose with the tip of my tongue. What's that all about? I have wasted tshe best part of my life trying. But I can't stop. You put it in my head. *Which one of us is going to be the first of us to be able to touch the tip of his nose with his tongue.* Now, whereas you are the reason for my disgusting behaviour you cannot blame me for yours. No way no how. Not a bar of it. Does that make sense? If we were umbilically tied, yeah, maybe. You've made your choices and I have to live with that. But I shouldn't have to suffer your consequences. Someone's after me, trying to kill me, in a clear case of mistaken identity. They think I'm you. I can't have that. I can't be run down like a dog for something you did. I'm not you. I'm a respectable member of the community. THE KING of the late night radio phone-in. By appointment to Her Majesty. Bloody MBE and all. I can't be going around trying to pick bogey with my tongue. That's not why the Queen gave me the gong. For years she was my number one fan. For years.

EFFRIES

Tuning in on a regular. Phoning in undercover. She'd rough up her voice and speak the pearly queen's english so that no one would recognise her. But she couldn't fool me. Called herself 'Betty from Bow Belles' and one night she calls up to talk about how recollections may vary and she accidentally on purpose goes:
God save me.
And I was like, *You're so gracious... and noble.* And she goes, *Just don't mention the next bit to the Scots.*

That's how I knew, without a shadow of a doubt that she used to tune in.

FORTY-TWO
What do you mean 'used to'?

JOOKS
Don't you know? Haven't you heard? The Queen is dead.

ELEVEN
She's kicked the bucket?

JOOKS
Yes. It's all 'long live the king' now.

FORTY-TWO
The Queen can't dead.

JOOKS
THE Queen can. She's only human after all.

FIFTY-TWO
So what, is it King William now?

JOOKS
No, King Charles.

FORTY-THREE
No way.

FIFTY-EIGHT
Least it's not King Andrew.

EIGHT
Ee-aye-addi-o
They're all the fucking same

TWENTY-FIVE
What this country needs is a revolution. Up the workers!

THIRTY-SEVEN
Said like those two striking miners kipping on your floor in halls.

THIRTY-SIX
The size of them.

THIRTY-SEVEN
The farts of them.

THRTY-SIX
There should be a law against it. Especially for minors.

TWENTY-FIVE
You and your divide and rule. Leave 'em alone. If the workers are united we will never be divided. We're comrades.

THIRTY-SEVEN
That's not what they were saying when your back was turned. They were saying 'ENOCH WAS RIGHT'.

TWENTY-FIVE
No way. I know them. They wouldn't say that.

THIRTY-SEVEN
Not when you're around. But Rass-O was like a fly on the wall in a room full of miners looking for student support for their strike. They had no idea that Rass-O is a white black man. He came round a while back, for old time's sake, and he was telling me. He didn't tell you because you

wouldn't believe him about anything that wasn't black and white, so he told me to tell you that they were blaming everything on 'the blacks'. Life, death and everything.

JOOKS
Memories. By the score. Flesh, blood and memories. That's the human condition. My memory ain't what it used to be. Huge chunks are just a blank. Your memories can solve this mystery and fill in my blanks. Which one of you holds the key to this manhunt? Why the big grin? What's so funny?

THIRTY-THREE
Nothing. I'm always smiling at some forgotten joke – the man with the golden grin, you know me. One of them 'two elephants fell off a cliff – boom-boom' ones. Don't worry about it. Why don't you hire a private detective to track down your lost memory? I can recommend one.

TEN
Uh please, mister, I'm really good at solving murders. Please can I be the detective?

JOOKS
No you can't. You're a suspect. I'm the detective.

TEN
A suspect? But I'm only a kid.

JOOKS
Everyone's a suspect.

FORTY-THREE
You're a suspect too then.

JOOKS
Apart from me.

SIXTY
Leave it out. I'm begging you. The past is never like it was. Leave it alone. What you remember you remember.

Everything else is contagious. Let it be.

JOOKS
Let it be? Someone's trying to murder me.

SIXTY
You've got until midnight. Call the cops. Whatever the cost to your career. Your life is more important than this sentimental journey down memory lane. Call the cops.

JOOKS
It might have escaped your notice that I'm black and not blue. The cops don't give a shit. National treasure or not. All they're interested in is fingerprints and DNA. Yours. Mine. They don't care when or who or what. Not even where. The moment I say someone's trying to murder me, they'll start investigating ME. And with you lot in my past I don't know what they'll find. There's nothing they can't prove with a little help from modern crimina technology. And then the shit will really hit my biggest fans. That's the jeopardy of celebrity. I'll lose everything. Everything will come crashing down. Not to talk of my liberty.

SIXTY
What about life, what about your wife and family?

JOOKS
They'll be 24 hours from Tulsa. Do you blame them?

THIRTY-THREE
Never mind blame, blame, blame, blame, blame. Gissa clue.

JOOKS
The only clue is this voice message.

TWENTY-SIX
Voice message?

THIRTY-THREE
Fucksake.

EFFRIES

TWENTY-SIX
On your answerphone?

THIRTY-THREE
Why didn't you tell us this in the first place?

JOOKS
I didn't want to prejudice your deliberations. Listen.

JOOKS, YOU BUMBOCLAAT, HAPPY DEAD DAY. WATCH NO FACE, SHITFACE. NOWHERE TO RUN, NOWHERE TO HIDE. I'M MAKING DUPPY. MAY GOD HAVE MERCY ON YOUR BATTYHOLE. MIDNIGHT, YEAH? YOU KNOW WHO.

JOOKS
You hear that?

TWENTY-SIX
Just about.

EIGHTEEN
You sure she's not a bloke who has lost his rag screaming?

TWENTY-FIVE
Was that screaming? I thought it was weeping and wailing. Definitely off her head though. Mad as hell.

JOOKS
Never mind screaming did you hear what she said? We are the only Jooks in the whole world. So it's me or you. And it's not me. You've got mail. Who do I forward it to?

THIRTY-THREE
Quality's shit but sounds vaguely familiar, I can't lie. Can't put my finger on it though. Oh, I know, it's Robert De Niro.

JOOKS
Why do you keep taking the piss? I've only got until midnight and all you can think of is jokes. Listen.

EFFRIES

JOOKS, YOU BUMBOCLAAT, HAPPY DEAD DAY... MAY GOD HAVE MERCY ON YOUR BATTYHOLE. MIDNIGHT, YEAH? YOU KNOW WHO.

JOOKS
Ring any bells? Which one of you lot is the battyhole she's after?

FORTY-THREE
Sounds like the woman who never liked you in the first place and liked you even less when her sister had that breakdown when you said love don't live here anymore. She always said she was going to make you pay.

FORTY-TWO
Exactly what I was thinking. It's got her dabs all over. Especially the way she says 'shitface'. She used to call you that all the time. Remember? Sounds just like her.

SIXTY
Let it be for crying out loud. The past is one long period drama. You have to live with it.

THIRTY-THREE
Or die with it.

JOOKS
I can't live like that. Shitting myself at the sound of a pin drop.

EIGHT
The more you eat the more you fart.

THIRTY-THREE
Call the cops and live or don't call the cops and die. At least the cops will put you behind bars where you'll be safe.

JOOKS
She's not going to want to murder an innocent man.

THIRTY-THREE
Maybe you can murder her first. I suppose if you have to do the time you may as well do the crime. Kill or be killed.

JOOKS
What do you take me for? I'm a law-abiding citizen.

TWENTY-FIVE
One sick individual.

JOOKS
What, me?

TWENTY-FIVE
No, you turnip, she who's trying to do you in.

THIRTY-THREE
For someone who is going to die on the stroke of midnight
you're like butter wouldn't melt. You sure this is it?

JOOKS
So help me God. I'm cool behind these locked doors. Come
midnight, Harry Houdini's going to have a job breaking in.

THIRTY-THREE
In that case why not just stay in your yard and ignore it?

JOOKS
That's what I'm saying. That's exactly what I'm doing. But
it's the side of me that's saying 'sweat' that's making me
panic, making me believe I've only got a few more hours,
which is making my bowels pay attention. If I ignore it
completely the floodgates open and empty, if you know
what I mean. It just churns and turns and churns.

TWENTY-THREE
Asthma or no asthma...

THIRTY-THREE
You want to do something about your imagination, mate,
it's running riot.

TWENTY-THREE
...I'll have whatever you're smoking.

EIGHT
Joker. Smoker.

JOOKS
Never mind me, this is all about you. Any thoughts? Any remembrances? You must have a clue.

THIRTY-THREE
Oh, here we go. It's Goldilocks and the three bears time.

SIXTY
You really believe this is judgement day?

JOOKS
You heard the woman.

SIXTY
That could mean anything.

JOOKS
Eh? How do you work that out?

SIXTY
How many times do people say that but they don't mean it? Someone screaming blue murder down a phone saying it's judgement day doesn't mean you're going to die tonight, does it? You've got far too many questions and not enough answers. I wouldn't take this judgement time thing too seriously if I were you. It doesn't add up.

JOOKS
Except for a moment of clarity. A fragment of memory in which I am squeezing the life out of this bloke. Strangling him to death with my bare hands. Squeezing and squeezing.

THIRTY-THREE
Your frigging imagination again. Get it seen to.

JOOKS
No, not my imagination, a snapshot of reality. A fragment

so vivid I can taste it. The taste of death. No more than a lingering echo of a remembrance but I can actually feel my hands around his throat. Choking him to death. Softly and slowly. Insistently. It feels so real. He is gasping and screaming and wriggling to get free and then. *SMASH!* My face crashes into the back of the driver's seat as the cab jolts to an abrupt emergency stop. I'm in the back seat with my hands round the cabbie's throat. Squeezing.

Oh my god, oh my god... IT WAS A NIGHTMARE. I'm so sorry.

The cabbie doesn't look like he believes me. He's gasping for air and he's para. He pulls this machete out from under his seat and waves it in my face.

GET OUT OF MY CAR. HELP. SOMEONE. CALL THE POLICE. THERE'S A STRANGER STRANGLER IN MY CAR.

It took two bills - cash - to calm him down and stop him screaming out the window. He even drove me to the cashpoint without turning his back on me. Says if I ever lay a finger on him again he'll break it. Break 'em all. Imagine if my missus heard about that. She would throw me out and tell me not to come anywhere near her bed again.

THIRTY-THREE
You are one screwed-up individual. Swear to god. You belong in a nut-house.

JOOKS
I'm allergic, you know.

THIRTY-THREE
Ha-ha. You must think you're funny.

TWENTY-TWO
How do you expect us to take this murder thing seriously when you've got time for jokes, Jooks?

JOOKS
No, for real, it's too real to be just my imagination. I've been racking my brain, trawling back through shimmering mists and scintillas of time trying to trigger that residue to deliver more but I'm not getting anywhere. That's why

I need your reverb. I've tried meditating, cool meditation. I've even been to a priest. You know that same one who got you to pack it in and give him all your weed TWO-TWOs.

TWENTY-TWO
That frigging con-man? Is he still around? You don't want to let him anywhere near your weed.

JOOKS
We wouldn't be here without him. He made it happen. And he reckons all will be revealed if I reach to the back of my mind, the outer reaches, the oblivion pavilion part where memories lurk, memories you thought were lost forever, the part where you lot live. In the outer reaches of my mind. And if you lot are there, yet recoverable, memories must be too. Is there a memory that explains my nightmare? Which one of you is a strangler? That would be the motive.

THIRTY-THREE
You've got some nerve, I'll give you that. You brought us all together on this zoom thingy-thingy to ask for our help in finding out who is trying to kill you and now you're admitting to a murder which you say you never did so it must be one of us. You're guilty of murder but you say it wasn't you and because you got away with it you're asking us to grass ourselves up so that you can grass us up. What have you been smoking? Have you lost your mind? Can you not see that if you're saying it was one of us... it was one of YOU. You're the one with your fingers round our throats and squeezing and squeezing and squeezing.

NINE
What's it like to murder someone, mister?

FIFTY-THREE
With your bare hands.

EIGHT
Here comes the chopper
To chop off his cock

JOOKS
It was only a nightmare. My fingers were round the throat of a dream I didn't commit. Squeezing the life out of it.

SIXTY
Let it be. Leave it out. Done is done.

JOOKS
I can't live with murder. Someone's got to own up.

SIXTY
Why not? If it wasn't you.

JOOKS
You ever heard of a conscience?

THIRTY-EIGHT
Nice car, nice gaff, nice wife, nice kids. A national treasure. Remember? You're living your best life. So sweet your trousers don't fit. Is that what you call a conscience?

JOOKS
I'm the one who has got to live with myself. I can do that if I confess to ol' bill that one of you done it.

TEN
Mister, you're as thick as two planks lengthways. Ain't you never heard of racial *diminiscration*?

SEVENTEEN
Yeah. Remember Cliff McDonald? One moment he's standing there minding his own business, chatting up the Hornsey High girls on the corner of Weston Park in the N8s, the next moment he's bundled into the back of a Black Maria by half a dozen coppers.

TWELVE
I was there. I remember. Lunchtime. One of the cops jumps out the van and grabs Cliff by the neck - squeezing and squeezing and another kicks him in the bollocks then his

seed starts to drip bleed. They bundle him in the van and a dinner lady runs up to say she has to go with them cos Cliff is only thirteen even though he looks like he's nineteen and that big afro makes him look even older. One of the coppers shoves her backwards and she falls over the kerb into the gutter and they drive off laughing.

THIRTY-SIX
Don't know what the cops did to him but he's never been the same Cliff since. To this day. Bumped into him recently. It's like they did the same thing to him as they did to that bloke in One Flew Over The Cuckoo's Nest.

SEVENTEEN
That's cops round here. Never tell them nothing. Don't give them a reason to send us to jail for no reason.

JOOKS
Let me shed a little more light on this darkened doorway of my soul.

THIRTY-THREE
Hallelujah!

JOOKS
Remember at the beginning of the pandemic, when everyone was having vivid dreams?

THIRTY-SIX
Pandemic?

JOOKS
Yeah. Lockdown. Whole nine yards. So surreal we struggled to put it into words. The streets were empty and the sky was a midnight blue that it hadn't been since the beginning of the industrial revolution. Apparently. The sound of silence. On the roads. In the skies. On and off the rails. Night after night after night on the phone-in all the lonely people isolating leaned on me. Caller after caller mourning the loss of their loved ones to COVID. It got to me. So much

so I had a blow-up with my neighbour. You know, the one who doesn't like me. Well, work booked me a session with that part-time priest, the one who took all your weed and then took all your booze off you and got high when he got you to get down. He concluded:

JOOKS has suppressed a traumatic memory from the past. It is the key to unlocking his current morose.

Look, I don't believe in all this 'seek and you shall hide' bollocks either, but I can't help wondering. Murder is trauma. It makes sense. You've suppressed it but it's still there.

THIRTY-THREE
So it could be the sister of a woman you spurned who is trying to kill you or it could be something to do with someone you murdered with your bare hands.

JOOKS
Not me. You. One of you got away with murder.

SIXTY
Don't look at me. I passed the baton firmly and completely. I didn't suppress anything. I would have remembered if I had.

THIRTY-TWO
Mate, I'm probably the only one here who really knows what you're going through. I burst out crying wherever I go. For no apparent reason. I'm supposed to have a suppressed memory and all. But I can't think what it is I'm supposed to have suppressed. It's suppressed, you see.

JOOKS
The nightmare always ends the same way. Strangling this bloke to death. I can feel him going limp and in the end he does the only thing he can do to save himself.

SIXTY
Oh my god, what?

JOOKS
I don't know.

THIRTY-THREE
Oh, for fucksake. You build it up and you build it up and then come crashing down to Goldilocks again.

JOOKS
What am I supposed to say? That's where the clarity ends. When I awake the nightmare's over and everything is a blur. All I know is that he's not trying to bite my balls off anymore.

FORTY-FOUR
Thank fuck for that.

EIGHT
Here comes the chopper.

JOOKS
I know. I know. I knew you were all going to laugh.

NINE
You're bonkers, mister. Really bonkers.

EIGHT
Ee-aye-addi-o
He's fucking queer

THIRTY-THREE
So this is it. You've brought us here to interpret a dream. Wasting my time to address a figment of your mad imagination.

JOOKS
You've got all the time in the world.

THIRTY-THREE
Are you having a laugh? Do I look like my name is Sigmund?

JOOKS
This ain't a joke. We're not here for a laugh. I've got until midnight. I've had no kip for ages. I keep shitting myself. Night after night after night. The moment I start

dozing I start suffocating. My neck tightens, my jugular is squeezed. That's why I hold on to my cock at night.

EIGHT
Hands off cocks and onto socks.

THIRTY-ONE
You really are a tosser. Didn't I say the little'uns shouldn't even be here, you wanker. You're corrupting their young minds with all this pulling out your cock business. You corrupt their minds, what do you think happens to us?

JOOKS
It may have escaped your notice but their minds are already corrupted. Nothing to do with me.

THIRTY-ONE
Squeezing your neck. Biting you balls off. Sort it.

FORTY-THREE
Exactly. Use your loaf. It's a freaking dream. The runt of an idle brain. You're not supposed to live by it. You are supposed to be a rational man but you're coming like a P-R-I-C-K.

TWENTY-SIX
A dream's just a dream. *Freud can't interpret them*, Frank Cioffi says. He reckons Freud's like Christopher Columbus saying he's the first one who discovered America. Tell that to the cowboys cos the Indians ain't listening. You wanna come to one of his lectures. It's worth a ticket price to get in. One day he goes, *I wasn't the scruffiest guy in the Army* and we all cracked up cos to look at him he must have been. But best of the lot. Head of the department at Essex.

FIFTY-TWO
Late great.

TWENTY-SIX
You what? Oh no.

FIFTY-TWO
Oh yeah. 'Fraid so. A while back now. You won't be getting into his lecture - love or money.

TWENTY-SIX
Dead. But how? Last time I saw him was at that symposium, *Freud and the Question of Pseudoscience*. He looked fine.

FIFTY-TWO
Clever man but spent his whole life proving Freud was a fraud. What a waste. Who wants to be known for that? You want to be a great philosopher not a great critic of someone else's philosophy.

EIGHT
I wanna be... Bobby's girl.

SIX
I wanna be a cowboy.

NINE
I wanna be famous.

JOOKS
Whispering ambitions. Seven-Up? You wanna open up?

SEVEN
W-w-w-wotcha.

TEN
You wanna paint yourself white.

THIRTY-NINE
Are you crazy? Have you lost your mind?

SEVEN
I'm only s-s-s-s-seven. I'm just a k-k-k-kid. Don't even kn-kn-know what I'm talking about. How am I supposed to know what's right from wrong?

FORTIES
Sad to hear, k-k-k-kid. Why d'you want to be w-w-white?

SEVEN
If I w-w-w-was white I would be h-h-h-happy.

FORTIES
White people are miserable too, y'know. Believe.

SEVEN
If I was w-w-white I wouldn't be hungry all the time. I wouldn't sh-sh-sh-shit myself all the time. If I was white this would be living in my own c-c-c-country.

FORTIES
Kid, you're not thinking straight. You'll see, when you're older. Meantime, you need to go to an African history class. Know yourself. Know what I mean?

TWENTY-TWO
Lyrics bredrin. Old Marcus Garvey. No one remembers him.

FORTIES
Don't forget you're a star. No matter what they say you are.

SEVEN
African h-h-h-h-history? But I'm only s-s-s-seven.

FORTY-SEVEN
And another thing, S-S-SEVEN, you're not mixed-race.

FIFTY-EIGHT
Kid, be who you want to be. Don't listen to anyone who tells you, you can't be. If you want to be white be white.

NINE
You keep shitting yourself. You wear a nappy?

JOOKS
Controlling bowel movements is a game of diminishing

returns. In my case it is the opposite. No matter how much I think I'm empty, the moment I turn my back there's a great flood of sewage. That's a whiff of my predicament.

ELEVEN
Really, really bonkers.

THIRTY-THREE
Thought you said you're the night watchman. You're supposed to be awake, not having nightmares.

JOOKS
Forty winks is all it was.

THIRTY-THREE
I don't care how many winks. You're working.

JOOKS
Wouldn't you be shitting yourself if someone was murdering you? I'm screwed if it comes out in any way shape or form.

TEN
Comes out the hole in your arse.

JOOKS
No, not shit, murder. The papers will make it look worse. No matter what. You know how they like to pull you down when you've made it to the top against all odds. They'll remind people that I really am from the hood. I don't know if I'll be able to cope with hero to zero all over the front pages. So come on, help me out guys, I can't be the only one with a snapshot of remembrance from having my cock sucked, I mean my balls bitten off?

THIRTY-THREE
This is your nightmare. Leave us out of it.

TWENTY-SIX
If you've murdered someone you're going jail for ever. You and your libido, eh? I bet it was over some girl and all.

EFFRIES

THIRTY-THREE
Look, don't get me wrong but you haven't got what it takes to kill a man. I know. Believe. Don't ask. Believe. I'm telling you now, you ain't got it.

JOOKS
What are you trying to say? What's that supposed to mean? You trying to say I'm fat?

THIRTY-THREE
I knew you would take it like this. That's why I didn't want to say anything. It takes a certain kind of mindset to be a killer. You ain't got that mindset. Once upon a time... But you ain't you no more. You ain't us. Not since your accident. You really are cross-eyed.

JOOKS
How did you know about my accident?

THIRTY-THREE
Never mind how. You ain't got the balls to be a murderer.

JOOKS
But I never told no-one. Only the missus. I had to tell her.

THIRTY-THREE
Some things are private. Some things are privates. You don't know one from the other until it makes you go cross eyed. Then you start seeing things differently.

TWENTY-TWO
Stir it up, my yute. Truth and rights.

JOOKS
You're a real shit stirrer. How come I don't remember you? Not a single memory. Where have you been? And how can you know about my accident thirty years in the future?

EIGHT
He's a cocksucker

43

THIRTY-THREE
Questions, questions. Far, far away. How I know? Trust me, you wouldn't want to know. Let's just say I can see into the future. And my money's on midnight.

JOOKS
I don't trust you. Not a word of you.

THIRTY-THREE
Think I care?

JOOKS
What am I supposed to do then when someone's trying to kill me?

FOURTEEN
Live fast, die young. Just like Jimmy.

TWENTY-FOUR
Screw Jimmy Dean. Just stop bunking off and nicking cars for chickie runs.

NINE
Why aren't you dead, mister, if you ain't had no sleep? And why ain't you got no grey hair if you're so old?

SIXTEEN
Bloody James Dean. I could have been somebody but for him.

TWENTY-TWENTY
If I had my teens again...

SEVENTEEN
Or I could have been nobody.

SIXTEEN
There I was happily not minding my own business.

FOURTEEN
Be a pretty corpse.

SIXTEEN
When I get this:
Jooks would do well if he could see his homework through a different lens than that of James Dean.
School report. Badge of honour. But the old man ain't going to see it like that. He will kill me when he comes home.

FORTY-EIGHT
If only you had taken that advice.

SEVENTEEN
Then I would never have starred in Killing Time. Barrie Keefe wrote that part for me cos he heard about a coloured boy at the NYT who thought he was a rebel without a cause.

TWELVE
What, you want to be white and all?

SIXTEEN
No. I just want to be James Dean. I'm going to get myself a red Harrington and a Porsche. You wait and see.

FORTY-EIGHT
James Dean was white, stupid.

SIXTEEN
Only on the outside.

JOOKS
NEWSFLASH. Text from my mate Webby. Haringey council have just re-named Black Boy Lane. After 300 years.

TWENTY-EIGHT
Yes. Yippie. Hurrah. Finally.

EIGHT
White Boy Lane has changed its name – Hallelujah!

TWENTY-NINE
Aarrhhh! Oh my god, oh my god, no please. Not a g-string.

No. Tell me I didn't see what I just saw. Tell me my eyes were deceiving me. In the name of the Lord, wipe it from my mind. Let me unsee what I just saw.

FIFTY-EIGHT
TWO-EIGHT, man, sit down. You can't get up in the middle of a zoom when you've got nothing on underneath.

TWENTY-EIGHT
I thought you said the zoom couldn't see I've got nothing on.

FIFTY-EIGHT
That's when you're sitting down.

TWENTY-NINE
A g-string? With that fat arse. That's going to scar me for life.

FORTY
Talking of the most horrible thing I've ever seen with my own two eyes, NINETEEN running like a pussy screaming 'Blood' is a sight to behold. What's it called again? That drama you were in. You know, the Swedish one.

FIFTY
Oh I remember that one. The one where you are a nurse in a hospital and this bloke starts spewing blood everywhere like a zombie and you come running out of the ward and, what was that you were screaming again?

NINETEEN
Blod, blod, en massa blod.

FIFTY
Yeah, that's it. It's on YouTube. Honestly, you lot should see it. You'll have kittens. The way NINETEEN moves in those clogs will make you weep. Like a fairy godmother.

THIRTY-FIVE
Acting was always your thing wasn't it? Oblong Box, Tennessee Williams, Diamonds Are Forever.

NINETEEN
They put us in the nativity the moment we got here, remember SIX? They couldn't wait. The moment me and Ollie arrived at Garden Suburb from Nigeria it was like two Christmases in one go. We solved the all-white school 'three wise men from the Orient' conundrum.

JOOKS
A-hhm, if we could just get things back on track. Remember someone's trying to kill me. Midnight. Who? Why?

THIRTY-THREE
So we're looking for something that proves you're a murderer.

JOOKS
And what about you?

EIGHT
He's a cocksucker.

THIRTY-THREE
What about me? I'm not at liberty to answer any questions.

EIGHT
Wogamatter?

THIRTY-THREE
Don't you have to establish if there's a body? No body no crime.

EIGHT
Browned off?

JOOKS
Oh, here we go. We all know how this one ends.

THIRTY-THREE
Never mind the ends. We'll all get there in the end.

EIGHT
Go black home.

JOOKS
What is wrong with EIGHT?

THIRTY-THREE
So let's go from the beginning. Where did you bury the body? Or did you dispose of it by other means?

JOOKS
Don't be stupid. Of course not.

THIRTY-THREE
Why not? Bodies don't simply disappear into thin air do they? So I'll ask you again, where did you bury the body?

JOOKS
For crying out loud I haven't killed anyone. I thought you said I didn't have it in me to kill. Besides, we've been locked down for yonks. I haven't had the time or the opportunity.

THIRTY-THREE
I knew we were gonna have beef with you.

THIRTY-FIVE
If you don't want your nose chop off, don't be nosey. That's what Victor Headley said this one night I come out of his yard in Hackney, back when the yardies turned it into a war zone, and lying there on the pavement is a finger.

FIFTY-FOUR
Flipping 'eck.

THIRTY-FIVE
Yeah, right, a finger. All fresh with blood and everything. Freaked me out. I ran back in. Called Asha. You know what he's like. Comes out all bad bwoy in his oversize Clicks, Kangol and shades. Middle of the night. He pulls out his pen knife and stabs the finger like a fork and, like he's Sherlock, lifts it up to the street light and, examining, concludes from the congealment that the finger was detached within the last hour. All cold and matter-of-fact

like it's just another day in the 'wild-wild east'of London.
We gotta call the cops, man.
Asha's like:
You must be crazy. You don't know whose finger it is. You don't know who detached it. Nobody's died. As far as you know. No body. Just a finger. Cow never know the use of him tail 'til the butcher cut it off. Not worth chopping your nose off over this.

JOOKS
Jeez. What happened to the finger?

THIRTY-FIVE
You'd have to ask Asha about that. He told me not to worry and that he would make sure that the finger was returned to its rightful owner. He wrapped it in a tissue and put it in his pocket. Imagine if I had stuck my nose in. Don't get involved. The consequences can be catastrophic.

JOOKS
WHY ALWAYS ME? No one else stumbles on a missing finger.
WHY ALWAYS ME? Not to talk of the Shoe Bomber.

FORTY-TWO
You all know he was living with us on Endwell Road in the SE4s.

THIRTY-ONE
Who?

FORTY-TWO
Richard. Richard Reid. Tried to blow up a plane.

THIRTY
No way.

JOOKS
Yes way. The Shoe Bomber. On the frontline.

THIRTY-THREE
Why d'you have to mention it? Do we need to know? Does it make you feel hard? Have you got an erection? You weren't

the only one saying *As-salaam alaikum* back then, y'know.

JOOKS
I've got nothing to hide.

THIRTY-THREE
And everybody needs to know how 'real' you are, yeah?

THIRTY-TWO
Richard was more *Farrakhan's a prophet so I think you oughta listen to what he can say to you*, and all that.

FORTY-TWO
Then he finds this muslim fringe thing, doesn't he, and the next thing he's mates with Osama Bin Laden and trying to set fire to his foot over the Atlantic. If you take off your shoes at airport security it's because of him.

SIXTY
Don't you think I know that when I fly overseas?

JOOKS
They don't make you do that any more.

THIRTY
He nicked my *Express Yourself* twelve inch. At our Free Nelson Mandela party. Same night he came out of jail after 27 years behind bars. Remember? One of the best parties ever? Day before I moved to LA. 48 hours later I'm maxing and relaxing and California dreaming with Dr Dre in Torrance with Donovan the dirt biker. Kicking it, you know.

JOOKS
I remember. I'm always telling people about how he had a Glock nine milly in each of the cabinets on either side of his bed depending on which side he was lying on when someone broke in.

THIRTY-THREE
Oh, here we go. Stiff cocky time again.

EFFRIES

THIRTY-TWO
Cali knows how to party.

TEN
Who's Dr Dre?

FORTY-THREE
No offence THIRTY but we ain't got time for Dre day and Stevie Wonder and all your other superstar mates.

THIRTY-THREE
Let's see if they're still your mates when we solve this murder.

FORTY-TWO
I'm standing barefoot in the departure lounge thinking, why didn't TWO-NINE just slap him one when he was pimping those two Polish girls he said were his sisters.

TWENTY-NINE
Richard who dosses round ours? Tall, light-skin. Mate of Mark's from down the road. That is heavy, dude.

JOOKS
You see. *WHY ALWAYS ME?*

FORTY-TWO
All over the news. In one photo he's under arrest in the back of some cop car and he looks up with one eye at the camera and he's got a beard and everything and one of those orange jumpsuits. It's the look, but I didn't know what I was looking for. Then one day I get this random email: *You might not remember me but I used to live next door on Endwell Road. All's well but this doesn't end well, I'm afraid. I'm just letting you know to expect a call from the tabloids. They've been sniffing around here looking for anyone who remembers your former housemate Richard Reid, the Shoe Bomber.*
But I don't know no Shoe Bomber, I thought. Then I googled that photo of him under arrest again. This time I knew what I was looking for. And there was no mistake.

THIRTY-FOUR
Fancied himself didn't he. Always did.

THIRTY-FIVE
Dumb enough to walk through Paris on a rainy day with a bomb in his heel.

THIRTY-THREE
Brave, though. You've got to give him that.

FORTY-SIX
I've thought about that over and over again as I'm putting my shoes back on in the departure lounge. I reckon it was a cry for help. I reckon he didn't have any intention of really blowing up that plane. Unless he really has done his nut in. The Richard Reid I remember from the SE4s...

JOOKS
Actually tried to blow up a plane. *WHY ALWAYS ME?*

THIRTY-EIGHT
That's what happens when olders don't school youngers properly? Guide them. Show them what's what and what the world's all about. It's like a jungle sometimes.

TWENTY-NINE
I should have mannersed him. But I'm not going jail for it.

FORTY-SIX
He's never coming out. He's got so many years left without parole he'll probably get a telegram from the Queen on his release.

JOOKS
No he won't. Like I said, Her Majesty is dead.

TWENTY-NINE
I still can't believe it.

TWELVE
The Queen. Dead. Feel like crying.

SIXTY
Weirdly enough, me too.

TWENTY-NINE
Shoulda mannersed all them bad bwoys in my yard. and shown them how the system works and how to navigate your way around this effries of a maze we call life, without going under.

THIRTY-THREE
Where you went wrong was in letting Richard get away with nicking your records to express himself with his full capabilities. That's why he's living in correctional facilities.

FORTY-SIX
What about my theory that he never intended to blow up the plane? That it was a cry for help from some mixed-up mixed-race kid caught in a whirlwind of mixed emotions in the mixed-up remix of contemporary Britain.

FORTY-THREE
Leave it out. This is no time nor the place for no expialidocious.

FORTY-SIX
No, hear me out. Richard used to go on about being black.

TWENTY-NINE
Wanted you to know he wasn't Greek. I bought my yard from his mum when she sold up to move out West. She didn't take him along on account of how he had beaten up his stepdad, some white guy he didn't get on too tough with. His mum thought she was bringing up a mixed-race yute but he was too black too much. 24/7. Brother Richard X. His mum didn't have a clue how to bring all that up. They call him the Shoe Bomber? Guess that's better than the Underpants Bomber.

SIXTY
That's the other bloke. Only a Nigerian, eh?

JOOKS
Oh no. My phone has just pinged. Message from you-know-who:

EFFRIES

JOOKS, YOU RAASHOLE. YOU READY TO DEAD? LOOK OUT, LOOK OUT. LOOK OUT. ME DEH 'BOUT. MIDNIGHT, YEA ? STINKFACE.

TWENTY-SIX
Sounds like she means it.

FORTY-FIVE
She's not messing about.

THIRTY-THREE
I'm getting worried for you.

JOOKS
Don't worry. I'm as safe as houses.

THIRTY-THREE
I think I know who that is. You should be worried. Walls won't keep her out. If she says midnight she means it. And when she gets hold of you, well, she'll eat your heart out.

JOOKS
Why won't you turn your video on? What are you hiding?

THIRTY-THREE
So you can see who I look like?

THIRTEEN
I murdered Remi.

JOOKS
What the f–!

FORTY-ONE
You. It was you.

NINE
Who's Remi?

EIGHT
Here comes the chopper...

WHAT WERE YOU THINKING? WHAT WERE YOU DRINKING? YOU'RE YOUR BROTHER'S KEEPER. THINE IS THE KINGDOM.

This is the missing piece of a puzzle. Déjà vu all over again.

LOOKS LIKE YOU. SOUNDS LIKE YOU. SMELLS LIKE YOU. IT'S EVEN GOT YOUR NAME ON IT.

I know it's got my name on it but it's not me.

BARE HANDS AND ALL.

How many times I got to say it wasn't fucking me?

WATCH YOUR FUCKING LANGUAGE. THIS IS A CHURCH FOR FUCKSAKE. NOW LET'S GO THROUGH THIS MURDER YOU SAY WASN'T YOU ONE MORE TIME. CONFESS YOUR SINS.

Please, I beg you. Why won't you believe me?

BECAUSE OF THE BLOOD ON YOUR HANDS.

But my hands are clean. See, no blood.

WHAT HAPPENED HAPPENED. NOTHING HAPPENED THAT WEREN'T SUPPOSED TO. WHATEVER HAPPENS HAPPENS EVEN IF IT AIN'T SUPPOSED TO HAPPEN TO YOU. HAPPENED WORSE THAN YOU EVER IMAGINED. IT'S WRITTEN IN THE STARS.

More bollocks.

I'M TRYING TO PROTECT YOU.

Protect me from what? You can't put this back in the past.

DO YOU MIND IF I TRY? AFTER ALL I USED TO BE A RABBI.

JOOKS
You murdered Remi?

TWENTY-NINE
Remi as in me and my baby brother Remi who died?

FORTY-FOUR
And you kept quiet about it all this time?

THIRTY-FOUR
You didn't say a word.

FOURTEEN
You killed Remi? You bastard. How could you? Why? I'm still feeling it. Cos of you. I wake up in the middle of the night crying. I can't concentrate when I'm in school.

SIXTEEN
Bollocks and you know it. Rock 'n' roll is your concentration. I can't concentrate cos of girls. I think about them all the time when I'm in class. It's not cos Remi was murdered.

SIXTY
Look, let's leave this in the past, man. None of us wants to relive it or even think about it. I don't want to hear that he was murdered. Let's just keep his memory alive.

JOOKS
I have a memory of him, must be from Vale Terrace, wearing his thick blue winter parka and giggling his head off.

FOURTEEN
He loved being thrown up in the air. He loved that.

JOOKS
That's my memory too. In his blue parka being thrown up high to the ceiling giggling.

THIRTEEN
That was the night before I killed him.

SIXTY
He was just eighteen months old.

JOOKS
I thought he died of a cot death? That's what I've remembered.

THIRTEEN
That's what they called it. They call everything a cot death nowadays. That's why I didn't say nothing.

THIRTY-SIX
Why? Why did you kill your own brother?

THIRTEEN
I didn't kill him for a reason.

TWELVE
You killed him for no reason?

JOOKS
For no reason? You're making this worse. You killed him for no reason?

THIRTEEN
If I could bring him back... if I could rewind I would. It was freezing that morning. I took Remi to the child minder off the Blackstock Road as usual before school. You know, Finsbury Park. Mummy gave me a shilling to get him some Farley's rusks. Well I nicked the rusks from the chemists (I didn't mean to) and, with the shilling or five new pence as they call it now, went and bought a bar of chocolate and a packet of KPs. Nuts, you know. Should have nicked them and all. I gave Remi a bite of the chocolate and a couple of nuts. Just a couple. How was I to know that I was poisoning him? It wasn't until a couple of weeks later in school when Molly reckoned he was allergic to nuts and how it makes his face come out in rashes and makes

him choke and throw up and nearly die that I realised I murdered my own brother with peanuts.

FOURTEEN
Molly's such a liar. There's no such thing as a nut allergy?

THIRTEEN
That's what I thought. So I ignored him. But then the doctors said that Remi choked on his own vomit in the cot and had a rash. In other words, I murdered him. Dead. My own brother. That's what I have to live with.

FORTY-NINE
You murdered Remi. I couldn't live with that.

THIRTEEN
Do you know what it's like when your mum comes home screaming, *REMI IS DEAD. REMI IS DEAD. REMI IS DEAD.*

FORTY-NINE
Oh no. This is a tragic memory. The worst. Eighteen months old. Can you imagine the shock for her when she went to the child minder's after work to collect him from the cot - the child minder told her he was sleeping - only to find him dead. Yet she still ran all the way to the John Scott Health Centre on Green Lanes - half a mile - in heels, Remi in her arms. Hoping against hope. You've got to feel for her. I don't know how she survived.

THIRTEEN
That's why I couldn't say nothing. They had to prise Remi from her arms at the Health Centre and she then ran all the way home, another half a mile, still screaming. I was in the front room watching telly and I could hear her wailing and gasping for air halfway down the road. She fell into my arms when she got in, out of breath, still screaming *REMI IS DEAD. REMI IS DEAD.* We went out looking for the old man. Me and her. He was supposed to be in an evening class at North London Poly, you know the one with the grey high-rise building on the Holloway Road.

FORTY-TWO
Still there. North London Uni now. It's a lot bigger. The tower block is still there. They've built so much around it.

THIRTEEN
Anyway, he wasn't where he was supposed to be.

FORTY-FIVE
How could you feed an eighteen month old peanuts? What's the matter with you? Where's your common sense?

THIRTEEN
But Remi loved peanut butter sandwiches. How was I to know?

FORTY-FIVE
Everybody knows about peanut allergies.

JOOKS
Nowadays, yes. But back then...

THIRTEEN
Never even heard of it.

TWELVE
Murderer.

THIRTEEN
Piss off. It was an accidental murder.

TWELVE
That's the point, stupid. Still fucking murder.

THIRTEEN
Don't call me stupid.

TWELVE
You murdered your own baby brother.

THIRTEEN
Say that again for no reason and I'll murder you, toerag.

SIXTY
Still can't live with it though. Wish you'd never told us this. This is all your fault, JOOKS. Raking up the past. There you have it, THIRTEEN is the murderer you're looking for. Satisfied? The blood on our hands is our own brother's.

JOOKS
Why would someone try to kill me over the death of my own brother? All these years later? It doesn't make sense.

THIRTY-THREE
Me, me, me, me.

FIFTY
The post-mortem said it was a cot death. I don't know about you lot but Remi's death is nothing to do with me.

THIRTEEN
I think about it every minute of the day. Haven't slept. I'm so tired I'd cut my own throat just to get some kip.

FOURTEEN
Cut your throat you kill me too, you plank.

FIFTEEN
Cut your throat and I'll murder you. Over and over again.

TWENTY-NINE
Cut your throat and you kill us all, moron.

THIRTEEN
I can't go on living without sleep. I'm cracking up. I'm crumbling. I've got to get to ga-ga. Nothing else matters.

TWELVE
You murdered my little brother.

THIRTEEN
Get lost. I didn't hear you go on about nothing when them cops split Terry Tarzan's head open? If I'm a murderer

they're murderers an' all but no one goes on about them.

SIXTY
Terry Tarzan? Terry's not dead.

TEN
Course he is, you pillock. They buried him in the cemetery. Go and have a look if you don't believe me. The old man wouldn't let me go. He reckons I'm too young for funerals. All the others was there. Boydie. Dino and Howard Malcolm was there and Raymond Tanner. That's how come we knew where to go when we bunked over the cemetery at night to piss on his grave. There were loads of flowers and that so we pissed on them and all. We had to so that Terry wouldn't come back and haunt us. We all knew the cops murdered him but who's gonna believe a bunch of kids?

SIXTY
Mate, you're mistaken. Terry's not dead. He got in touch with me just the other day. Out of the blue. We've been sending messages, back and forth, about the old days.

FORTY
Mate, YOU'RE mistaken. Terry's been dead ages. Don't know why we still talk about him. Guess, you know, he was kinda different. Guess people don't forget you if you're 'king of the jungle'. But that was his real name to be fair.

FIFTY
Man of mystery wasn't he? Of undefined racial heritage. Lived up Endymion Road. Are you sure he was murdered?

TEN
I was there, so there.

FIFTY
What, when it happened? How come?

TEN
We was all there. Terry. Me. Harry Boy, Alex, Duggie, Fizz

and Charlie Chin. Trying to get lost like we was told to by our parents. And then the cops started chasing us for no reason. Charlie Chin reckons it's cos of the way we look, but I reckon it was cos we was smashing them windows over by the dogs.

FIFTY
Smashing windows. Why?

TEN
I don't flipping know. It was a hot day. We was just hanging around not doing nothing. Wasting time. By the petrol station over by the entrance to the dogs.

THIRTY
Ain't like that no more. All that's gone. Petrol station's gone. Car wash has gone. And even the dogs... that's gone and all. That Shell station is some DIY place now.

THIRTEEN
Harringay Stadium. Greyhound racing. Gone?

THIRTY
Yeah. To the dogs. It's a housing estate now.

FOURTEEN
Tell 'em, TEN, how the cops split Terry Tarzan's head open and got away with it. It was boiling, weren't it, that day.

TEN
Yeah, really hot. And we weren't doing nothing. Just standing around, kicking stones and that, minding our own business. And then... you know that old factory on the other side of the entrance to the dogs from the petrol station, the one that's just standing there empty since they closed it down?

THIRTY
Yeah, that's gone too. Everything's gone.

NINE
I remember when it was open and all these lorries used to

drive in and drive out.

TEN
Yeah, but they shut it down. Locked the gates. Ain't been no one in there for ages. And we can't even bunk over cos the walls are too high.

SIXTY
That will be the reason why the walls are so high.

TEN
Like I said, one moment we was kicking stones, messing around, you know. Then *CRASH!* One of us (not sure who) picked up a rock and flung it over the gate and that and one of the big windows of the building in the yard went *SMASH!* It was like *WOW!* We never knew none of us could do that. So we all had to try.
CRASH! CRASH! CRASH! CRASH!
We were having so much fun we didn't even think about the cops. We was on Green Lanes, the high street, with people passing up and down and all the traffic and that. Didn't even stop to think about it. Felt so good to smash them windows. We smashed all the bottom ones and was trying to smash the top ones when somebody shouts *COPS!* Nearly shit meself. There was this copper coming towards us from the Green Lanes end. Someone shouts *RUN!* And we all run down the other end, you know, to that other gate to the dogs down by where Harry Boy and them lot live. Cos there's that hole in the fence we can get through. Anyway the cop's running after us and we was running so fast for our lives, like bleeding greyhounds, he couldn't catch us. I was thinking, this is too easy. It's bound to be a trap. *THERE'S BOUND TO BE A COPPER AT THE OTHER END!*
Sure enough this other copper appears out of nowhere standing in front of the hole in the fence. And we're trapped between the copper and the other copper who is still coming after us. And someone (dunno who) shouts *SCARPER!* and we all leg it in different directions and that. It was every man for his self. Duggie scarpered with me round the back of the car wash and we got away. Somehow.

EFFRIES

We ran and ran and ran and ran and kept running until Duggie got so tired we had to stop outside Titch's house on Stanhope Gardens, you know, on the other side of the railway line. Titch wasn't in so we jumped over his back garden fence to Antonio's and called up to his bedroom window. He popped his head out and looked down at us and cos we were out of breath and all sweaty and scared and that, he wouldn't open up. I shouted:

Open up, you cunt. I'm gonna kill you if you don't let us in right now. I'll fucking kill you, you wait and see.

Titch was all bad and brave looking down from upstairs.

If you kill me I'l tell my mum and dad, he shouted back.

And then Duggie, you know how bad and brave he is, even though he's only little, starts singing:

EIGHT
You're a fucking cunt
You're a fucking cunt
Ee-aye-addi-o
You're a fucking cunt

TEN

And then Antonio's old man comes out from having his tea, with a fork in his hand, jumping up an down and shouting:

Who's a fucking cunt?
Who's a fucking cunt?
Ee-aye-addi-o
Who's a fucking cunt?

TEN

And he comes after us, see, trying to jook us with the cutlery and that. We had to run for our lives. Over the next garden fence. And the next. We leg it round the corner to Moosh's and jump a couple of fences into his garden and wait until it's all quiet and that. When Moosh comes round the back into the kitchen we tap the window for him to let us in. He nearly shit himself but he did open up the back door. We told him the whole story and we was laughing our heads off playing Monopoly and that and, before we knew it, it was dark and we didn't think there would be any more cops on the streets looking for us so we left Moosh's and Duggie went home and I went home. I'd only just walked in when there's a knock on the door. *Shit!* I was shitting meself. How the ol' bill know where I live unless one of the others grassed me up? I was about to jump out the back and run away from home again, third time in a row, but then I see through the front door glass that it was Tarzan. He was shitting his self an' all. I see it in his eyes as soon as I opened the door. The back of his shirt was soaked in blood an' that. So much blood I just knew he was going to die. It was coming from the back of his head. He says that one of the coppers chased after him and was catching up to him, so he climbs up on the roof of one of them garages behind the petrol station and, cos he's only little, he got up the drainpipe easily but the cop with his big old boots couldn't get up the drainpipe so instead he picks up a brick and chucks it. Splits the back of Terry's head open with it but he still manages to get away.

JOOKS
What!

TEN
Yeah, and now Terry comes round shitting his self, bleeding all over the place, scared he was going to die, and asking what he should do cos he reckons the ol' bill must have told all the hospitals in the area to watch out for a kid coming in with his head split open so they can arrest him for breaking windows. And he didn't want to go home cos his mum would do her nut if she saw all the blood on his shirt. I had to tell him to fuck off cos if my old man woke up from all the whispering at the front door and saw Terry covered in all that blood he'd kill me. So I told him to hush himself up and piss off and I shut the front door on him and, I swear, that's the last I saw of him.

SIXTY
I keep saying Terry's not dead. Nobody murdered nobody. I've been texting him. Look, it's on my phone. The convo.

TEN
Blimey. Then who's that buried in the cemetery?

SIXTY
How do you expect me to know if you don't know?

JOOKS
Maybe the question we should be asking is, who is that texting you if it's not Terry Tarzan?

NINE
Tarzan's ghost! You sure you pissed on his grave?

THIRTY-THREE
Oh no, not ghosts and all.

TEN
Take the mickey if you want but I've seen one. A real one, so there. A girl. A baby girl. That's why I can't sleep.

NINE
I've seen her too.

TEN
Yeah. You can't tell me she's not a ghost. I can put my hand right through her.

ELEVEN
I've seen her too. She's really scary.

SIXTY
I warned you, JOOKS. I told you, didn't I, to be careful where you're going with this. Tread cautiously. See what you've gone and dug up that you didn't need to trouble. Let lying dogs sleep.

JOOKS
Life and death cannot simply be buried in the mist of time.

THIRTY-THREE
You do come out with some nonsense. I'll give you that.

THIRTY–SEVENTH
Hear the man out. He walks in our shoes. We ain't walked in his.

THIRTY–THREE
He's walking like a pussy with an MBE. In my shoes.

JOOKS
Just because I couldn't kill a man?

NINE
What's an MBE?

THIRTY–THREE
No, because you're rich and fat. You've become a white guy in your nice neighbourhood. There ain't no real you left in you.

TWELVE
If you can't beat them you may as well be them.

SIXTY
Is this the fabled Battle of Hermitage Road you kicked off?

TWELVE
That's where you're wrong. It was Nick Nicolau who chucked the first rock. Ollie had to kick his head in.

TWENTY–EIGHT
No reason?

TWELVE
I was just coming home from school and he calls out from across the road right in front of the offie:
Oi, nig-nog.

ELEVEN
It's always cos we're black.

TWELVE
I ignored him. Then he picked up a rock and flung it. Smack in me face. Coulda killed me. Cos you know if it hits you

right above the bridge of the nose you die. Did you know that? Right smack on the bridge of the nose. I screamed my head off. Ran home bleeding.

THIRTY-THREE
And crying.

SIXTY
Yeah, we've all got the scar to prove it. Right here, see? On the bridge of my nose. But why? You used to spar. Nicholas and Ollie were best mates. Why would he start a race war with you? And also why didn't you answer when he called? How come you acted like you had never seen him before in your life?

TWELVE
For a laugh. It was just a laugh. So I go home bleeding and the old man tells me to shut up and tell him what happened.

THIRTY-THREE
And to stop your crying before he claps you one.

TWELVE
So I tell him the story and he tells Ollie to deal with it.

EIGHTEEN
N15s and N17s all over. Shit or get shat on.

TWELVE
So Nicholas and them are still hanging out by the offie all casual like and Ollie goes up to him:
OI, BIG MAN, I'M GONNA HAVE TO HURT YOU FOR WHAT YOU DONE TO MY BRO, Y'KNOW.
Nicholas goes:
I'm shaking all over and wobbles his legs like he weren't really shaking about nothing.
Ollie goes:
SHUT IT. YOU'RE ONLY MAKING IT WORSE.
Nicholas made it even worser.
Wogamatter Ollie, you browned off?

EFFRIES

Ollie weren't in no wogamatter mood.

WHO DO YOU THINK YOU'RE TALKING TO? YOU THINK YOU CAN STAND THERE AND TAKE THE PISS OUT OF ME COS I'M COLOURED? IT'S COMING LIKE YOU'VE FORGOTTEN WHO MAN ARE. LIKE MAN'S SOME PRICK.

You would never have known they were best mates, the way Ollie kicked the shit out of Nicholas. Never seen nothing like it. Left-right, left-right, left-right - feet and fists and an Ali shuffle an' all. But Nicholas won't stop giving lip. Lips all swollen, one of his eyes all closed up and his face all dirty from all the crying. Ollie tells him over and over and over again:

STOP TAKING LIBERTIES.

But it's like Nicholas don't know how to.

MY OLD MAN'S SORTA BIBLICAL WHEN IT COMES TO SHIT LIKE THIS. AN EYE FOR AN EYE IS WHAT HE PREACHES. SO I'VE GOT TO SMASH YOUR FACE IN. WITH A ROCK. LIKE YOU DID JOOKS. THAT'S THE WAY THE OLD MAN SEES IT. I'VE GOT TO DO IT. I AIN'T GOT NO CHOICE. TO SQUARE THINGS UP.

Course you got a choice. You can't blame your dad. You've always got a choice even if you don't choose. If you smash my face in it's all your fault.

Ollie squares things up all right and nearly kills him. Then Xenophos runs across the road to tell his mum that Nicholas is getting the shit kicked out of him and she comes running out of her front door with a frying pan to fight for her son, screaming her head off at the sight of his bloody nose broken and leaps on Ollie and whacks him one in the back of the head. He goes limp and start's frothing at the mouth. I thought she'd killed him. Nicholas manages to wriggle free and gets up all bad and brave and kicks Ollie in the bollocks as he lies on the ground still in shock.

Next time I'll kill you, you black bastard.

It takes Ollie a moment to recover but when he does he just lays into them - Nicholas, Xeno, the mum... The lot of them. Then their dad pulls up in his old Austin Cambridge. Remember, sky blue with a cream stripe running along each side. So I run home, round the corner, to tell the old man that now Nicholas's dad has joined in the fight and the old man comes out and, before Nicholas's dad is able to say two words, knees him in the bollocks and punches him to the ground. And that's when it all kicks off. Before you knew it, it was whites this side, blacks that side. Raymond Tanner's old man comes out with his grandad, rolling up his sleeves, like they'd been waiting for a punch-up like this for ages, and his mum and his nan with their kitchen aprons on join in from the pavement shouting:

Punch him in the face. Kick him in the bollocks. Strangle him.

Then Will Greenaway's big sisters all come out and start fighting the Tanners, their next door neighbours, like they had been waiting to punch 'em for ages. And then Peter Gutteridge's old man comes out and runs up the road like Popeye, sleeves already rolled up. And Carl and George's old man comes out with Carl and George beside him. And Gutteridge's mum shouts out from her upstairs window:

Why don't you piss off. This area used to be nice before you lot came. You could leave your back door open. It's like cowboys and indians now. Why don't you fuck off back to your own country.

EIGHT
If you're white
you're all right,
If you're brown
stick around,
But if you're black
Get back.

NINE
Why do we always have to be the bad guys? Why can't we be the cowboys for a change?

TWELVE
And then that little mixed-race kid, Saddlehead, who used to live down the road wanders right into the war zone wondering what's going on and Valentine from round the corner shouts:

Whose side are you on?

Before he could say nothing his mum comes out of nowhere and yanks him by the arm and drags him out of it.

Didn't I tell you to stay away from them lot, Saddlehead?

EFFRIES

At the same time Raymond Tanner's nan is doing her nut that she didn't want none of '*them lot*' in her house again. And when one of the other neighbours points out that she takes them lot's children as a child minder she goes:
I'm not prejudiced. There's good and bad in everybody. It's just this lot.

ELEVEN
She's never really liked me and Ollie since her husband had his face smashed in on the buses by some coloured kids. Aftet that we weren't allowed to go in their house to play with the Scalextric in their attic.

TWELVE
By now everybody's fighting. The whole street. And shouting and screaming. And the dogs are barking. And cars are honking. And the kids are charging up and charging down. *CHAAAARGE!* Then in the middle of it all, along comes this bloke with a cross to bear saying:
Peace and love. The Lord is my shepherd. Green pastures. Still waters. Follow Jesus. And Ollie tells me to follow him. But I never was much good at listening to my elders.

FORTY
Same as me when I was your age.

TWELVE
When were you ever my age?

FORTY
Believe it or not.

THIRTEEN
Didn't even know we was living in a war zone.

FIFTY-FOUR
Everything goes wrong in Tottenham. Buckets and spades. If we had moved anywhere else back then, who knows. But Tott-*Nam*? Well, you ain't going to win against Ho Chi Minh.

TWELVE
Not even in our own country.

EFFRIES

FIFTY-SEVEN
Wasn't much of a palace was it, Vale Terrace. Compared to the bedsit on South Park Road it was a mansion with twice as many rooms. We had the whole of the two-down.

TWENTY-SEVEN
People upstairs walked right through our downstairs to go up the stairs to their bit. No privacy. But that was all the old man could afford with five boys. The landlord, Mr Aziz, had a turban and whenever new tenants came to view the flat upstairs he would buy us a box of jaffa cakes to get lost.

FIFTY-EIGHT
Prospective tenants would think they were moving into a quiet house with no noisy kids. What a shock, eh? Five. All boys.

FORTY-SIX
We'd only been there a few minutes when there was a knock on the front door. Remember?
Fancy coming out for a game?
It was the kids outside.

THIRTY-SEVEN
And that was it. Our fortunes were umbilically tied to theirs forever.

SEVENTEEN
Rough at home. Rough on road. I can't wait to see the back of these days.

FOURTEEN
School is a bloody circus and we're in the lion's den. We don't stand a chance in learning nothing.

FORTY-SIX
Wait 'til you're my age. You've never had it so good. Things are going to get worse. Believe. You're in a circus, I'm in a zoo.

FOURTEEN
But you're out. You're in paradise. What could be worserer?

TWELVE
The NF keep coming round stirring.

THIRTEEN
Remember when those little girls across the road come out their house chanting 'wogs out'? Really hurts.

FIFTY-SEVEN
Yeah, but remember that girl you used to run after, the one who went to that school for clever girls up in Stamford Hill.

THIRTEEN
Debbie.

FIFTY-SEVEN
Yeah, that's her. Debbie. Remember how her step-father chased you down the road with a kitchen knife telling you to clear off whenever you knocked on her door. Remember?

THIRTEEN
How could I forget? It hurts the most. Still. But I love her.

SIXTEEN
Love. Is that what you call it?

FOURTEEN
You can't love her. Her old man's a flipping racist.

SIXTEEN
And you just take it.

SEVENTEEN
Chased by some fat bloke telling you to stay away from his daughter and you going back there the next day and every single day trying again, that's embarrassing. What, are you hoping that he'll change his mind and start seeing you as his future son-in-law. You believe that, I'm a coconut.

FOURTEEN
If I still cared about her I'd go round there and knock his

block off. He's NF through and through.

FIFTEEN
He needs to fuck off back to Trinidad where he comes from.

ELEVEN
Remember Richard Friend and his mate Rusty Balls? Got their heads kicked in that time over the rec when they picked on thata coloured kid, Angus McLeod and beat him up. Three against one cos Timothy Friend brought his cricket bat. And they chase him out the rec. They laughed and made fun of him as he ran. Richard goes:
If he's the best fighter in his school I wouldn't like to see the worst.
And Rusty Balls goes:
His family's so dumb his mum takes a bath in Fairy Liquid.

TWENTY-FOUR
Didn't Angus run out of the rec with a rope round his neck?

FIFTY-ONE
They were going to lynch him?

ELEVEN
No, hang him. They were gonna murder him. From a tree. I had a feeling it weren't over, though. I was watching them park gates. Sure enough Angus comes back floating like a butterfly with his two big brothers at his side. Rusty Balls and the Friends must have seen them at the same time out of the corner of their eyes cos they just froze.

TWELVE
They should have run for their lives. Any fool would.

ELEVEN
Angus doesn't waste no time. He kicks the shit out of the Friends and Rusty Balls. One at a time. His big brothers just stood there making sure it was a fair fight

THIRTEEN
First time I saw karate this was, before Bruce Lee.

ELEVEN
Angus stands sideways like he's on guard with his feet apart and his knees slightly bent. And he jumps ten feet in the air and does this somersault and lashes out at Rusty Balls with his left foot and catches him under the chin and leaves him gasping for air on his knees.

THIRTEEN
Ten feet. What have you been drinking?

ELEVEN
No, honestly, he's gone bonkers. Ain't no stopping him. Never seen fists so fast. It was amazing. Chops to the neck and the face. Rusty Balls was choking with Angus's foot on his throat. When it looked like he was dead, one of the older brothers pats Angus on the arm to tell him that's enough. Angus did as his brother told him and stopped dead on time.

EIGHTEEN
What about the Battle of Turnpike Lane? That's a race war an' all. When the NF and the BNP marched through. All rocks and bottles and smoke bombs. What a bundle. Me and Stelly were in the thick of it when it all kicked off. Bang in the middle of no-man's land. Like Cannon Street station, it was all Whitechapel this way Blackfriars that way.

NINETEEN
That was the first time I ever felt like this is my country and that the ends is worth fighting for.

TWENTY-FOUR
Still not how it used to be in the ends. They've blocked up a couple of roads and killed the traffic. Amazing. Nice and quiet. But where are all the kids on the streets like we used to be? Where are the ones like us lot getting up to no good and where are the good kids sitting on their front step or playing hopscotch? Where are the kids riding their bikes and playing ball games under the NO BALL GAMES signs

on the estate? What was the point in blocking off the roads if the kids don't come out for some fresh air so they can link up to learn about the streets and what's up and allow their parents some quality time together?

FIFTY-NINE
Yeah, I know what you mean. Heard a couple people got stabbed at a blues down in that part that used to be the Maynards ᴗine gums factory. It's all artists' studios now. Really trendy. Sweet little area. Nice vibe. Not like it was.

FORTY
Kids on the street or no kids on the street, wish it was like that when we were living there.

FIFTY-SIX
Yeah, but then we wouldn't have been able to afford the rent. Hermitage Road was a dump. Let's face it.

FORTY
Morning, noon and night. There weren't no two households both alike in dignity in fair Harringay where we lay our scene.

FIFTY-FIVE
We were always on the streets. Especially on Sundays. Straight after lunch all the kids would get kicked out of the house and the parents would close all the windows, *heh-heh.*

NINE
So they don't hear us making a racket in front of the house.

FIFTY-FIVE
If you say so.

FIFTY-SIX
Remember The Battle for Clissold Park? When we went with Woodberry Down to capture the park from them Hackney boys. TEN, remember?

FIFTY-SEVEN
I was tweeting about that just the other day.

NINE
What's tweeting?

TWENTY-SEVEN
I don't remember that at all.

FIFTY-SEVEN
Am I imagining it?

TEN
When we got there and saw the size of them we couldn't believe it. They were grown men. Twice the size of us. And they had cricket bats and bicycle chains and we had to run for our lives but they were much faster than us and there was much more of them than there were of us and they had razors so when they caught us they scalped us.

FOURTEEN
It was the twins on Vale Road, weren't it? It was them who started it and told us lot that we better be there to back them. They're mad them two.

FIFTY-SIX
Like the Krays. In and out of borstal. Always trouble. Trouble always.

TEN
We didn't stand a chance against Hackney. They kicked the shit out of Peter Guttermeat and then they scalped him when they caught him cos Duggie tripped him up so he wouldn't be last when they were chasing after us.

THIRTEEN
Someone's always getting the shit kicked out in our ends.

TEN
First time I ever heard about racial disminicration I couldn't

even pronounce it. Last summer. Some TV programme.

TWENTY-FOUR
Hold up, weren't you a stick-up kid?

TEN
We was all stick-up kids.

EIGHT
Stick 'em up your bum
Stick 'em up your bum
Ee-aye-addi-o
Stick 'em up your bum

NINE
I said, stick 'em up!

TEN
We was angels with dirty faces. Wise guys.

NINE
Stick 'em up. Did you hear what I said? Stand and deliver.

ELEVEN
Usually that's all you've got to say. Everybody knows the drill. *Stick 'em up* - it's not a question it's a commandment. Which means you ain't got no choice even if you're catholic.

TEN
Catholic boys are weeds. Everybody knows that. They really are. You should see them in their school uniforms. All you have to do is go *BOO!* and they stand and deliver. It's easy. Usually.

ELEVEN
Big head. Skinny legs. St Mary's blue and yellow trim.

TEN
And he wore glasses. For crying out loud to be robbed.

NINE
Stick 'em up. I mean it this time.

TEN
He just stood there shaking his head. Refusing.

FORTY
Ollie told you, didn't he, not to go sticking up kids on your own. Even if they're catholic. He warned you. You see, sticking up isn't as easy as it looks. He told you. But you're too hard of hearing when it comes to listening to your elders. He knew you weren't ready. Leave it to the pros. Now it's too late. You've got yourself a handful. What are you going to do? The kid is refusing to stand and deliver. What are the rules when some kid looks like he's fed up with being pushed around, like he ain't having it no more? What are you supposed to do?

NINE
Listen, I'm letting you off this time. Stick 'em up like you're supposed to next time.

TWENTY
And that was it?

FOURTEEN
Aren't you forgetting he called you 'chicken'?

NINE
Why would he do that?

FOURTEEN
And then walloped you one on the jaw? Look, I've got the scar here to prove it. Still there. After all these years. See?

FIFTY
Oh, that's what that scar is. I've sometimes wondered.

FOURTEEN
It's a reminder. That's why I remember. He whacked you

one didn't he?

NINE
I'm the one who was there.

FOURTEEN
He ate you alive and you took it. If you had had the guts to knock him out cold...

NINE
I didn't want to hurt him.

FOURTEEN
Didn't want to hurt him? Whose side are you on anyway?

NINE
I let the guy off this time and I thought it was over and everything was quits. Anyway, the next day, we was all walking home from school, past St Mary's, and when we turn the corner by the cop shop the whole of their school was waiting for us on the other side of the road. It didn't look right but we thought it was a fire drill or something. And there was this coloured boy, see, standing in the middle of the road like he weren't afraid of nobody, not even no cars. Didn't even know coloureds were catholic. It wasn't until we were right in the middle that the coloured boy goes *CHAAARGE!* and the entire school come after us. We ran for our lives.

FORTY-NINE
I guess Ledaker was right about you. That gangster business.

JOOKS
It'll be amazing to hear more of these old time stories about how you really were once upon a time, when I've got more time. Now back to how you got myself in this mess? Some woman is looking for revenge for what you did.

SEVENTEEN
Why are you looking at me? My virginity is still up for

losing. You know. I ain't broken no heart. I ain't even kissed a girl. Not a proper kiss. Do you mind telling me who I lose it to and when? How long I got to wait to make love not war? And how will I know what to do when I do it?

TWENTY-FIVE
And spoil the surprise? Wait your turn like everybody else.

TWENTY-ONE
Make zoom-zoom not boom-boom. This is not a shag palour. And by the way, even if this is a virtual room, you stink of desperation.

TWENTY-THREE
Oh, you smell pussy too?

THIRTY-EIGHT
You've got your mind on it and you've got it on your mind too much. It'll get you killed.

JOOKS
Who do you lot think you are? Great balls of thunder? You're the reason someone's trying to kill me.

FIFTY
One thing you haven't considered. Maybe she's trying to kill you because you're a witness and you don't even know it. I don't know if you know this but you did witness a murder, you know. That time at The Orange Tree in Friern Barnet. Remember, FIFTEEN?

FIFTEEN
What, when it all kicked off? There weren't no murder there.

FIFTY
Do you not remember when Stelly got stabbed in the neck? Weren't you trying to show off to some girl?

TWENTY-NINE
No one who was there is ever going to forget that. That

night we ended up with our own blood on our hands.

FIFTY-FIVE
I think I remember. The Orange Tree's a Tesco Express now.

FIFTEEN
It was kill or be killed.

FIFTY-THREE
So you are an eyewitness. What do you remember seeing?

FIFTEEN
None of your frigging business.

SEVENTEEN
There was broken bottles flying all over the place and people getting stabbed.

SIXTEEN
What I remember is that you were lucky to get out alive. Stelly's blood was everywhere. The whole side of his head was covered in it. It looked like they had cut off his ear. But it was only a stab in the neck.

JOOKS
Only a stab in the neck. Kill or be killed. Have you lost your frigging mind? What world are you lot living in?

FIFTEEN
It weren't my fault. I woke up that morning thinking:
Boy, this is gonna be one of them lovely days so you better enjoy it. Live it like it's the last day of your life.
And it nearly was. All cos of Doros. Flipping Doros. Thing that gets me is that he isn't even one of us. He's more greaser than ted. No duck's arse, nothing. But he hangs around us over at The Grange waiting for a wrong move. He's into the music, see, the fifties, you know. But I don't trust him. You can never tell whether he's laughing with you or at you. I mean, what's an eighteen year old with a Transit van doing hanging round teddy boys? Anyway,

a wop-bop-a-loo-mop-a-lop-bam-boom, we're all at The Grange just hanging around one evening and I'm trying to chat-up this girl, Judy, who's always there and I know she fancies me but I don't know how to ask her out, you know, in case she says no. And Doros shows up in a state, huffing and puffing.

You lot better come to The Orange Tree in Friern Barnet with me to sort out these blokes.

He says he's had a bust-up with a couple of guys in a pub who are cruising for a bruising. I never even heard of Friern Barnet. But he tells us there's only a couple of them and there's like five or six of us teds and so we go in his van and as we're parking up outside the pub Doros suddenly asks:

Where's your fucking tool?

And I'm like, *What fucking tool?*

And Doros goes *This fucking tool.*

And he pulls out these brass knuckle dusters. And we're like *FUCK!* cos we ain't never seen real ones before. So we go in the pub, hands in pockets like we're all tooled up and, before you know it, it's like one of them movies when it kicks off in a saloon. One moment Doros is nose to nose with this skinny guy who, seeing us lot behind him, isn't looking a scrap. But Doros isn't having none of the peace and love and white flag. He is screaming blue murder.

You cunt, you fucking cunt. What you going to do now, cunt face?

Next moment this coloured guy comes in, half-caste, you know, steps into Doros's face and tears it up.

Who do you think you're talking to? Who do you think you are? Coming in here all bad and brave. What are YOU going to do?

My boy must have been the cock of the town cos the whole thing switched. Suddenly we was surrounded. I didn't even notice that the guys on the pool tables had stopped playing and were standing upright and holding their cues the wrong way round like baseball bats. I didn't notice neither that all the girls had slipped away into the other bar. I was too busy trying to look tough to realise that it was us, the five of us, against the whole pub. We were kids. They were GBHers. Skinny threw the first punch.

BAM!

Right between Doros's eyes. If Doros had gone down and stayed down it might have ended there. He would have still got a good kicking but the rest of us would have got away with a few slaps, one or two digs in the back and a bottle to the head and maybe a toepunt up the arse an' all. And that would have been that. Doros on the other hand goes:

BAM!

Right back in skinny's face with the dusters.

BAM!

Right in the coloured guy's face.

BAM! BAM! BAM!

All hell breaks loose.

Kill the cunt. Kill him.

To be honest, hell is one big blur. It was mayhem, a proper rumble. My very first. Everything in the place got smashed – glasses, bottles, cue sticks. It all happened so fast. I'd always dreamed of being in a proper rumble but I never thought it would be life or death. Thankfully most of the tables and chairs were raining down on Doros. And there's a knife, Someone's stabbing everybody in the chaos. Somehow I managed to pull the cue stick out my arse and grab hold of Stelly. He was being kicked from one pair of Doc Martens to the next. He's been stabbed in the neck. Turns out I've been 'stabbed' too.

Your arse is bleeding Stelly shouts as we leg it from the scene. He's got one hand on the top of his head, holding it down, in case it falls off. With his other hand he's trying to stop the blood flow from his neck but its seeping through his fingers. Don't know where we're running. Just as far away as we can get.

If only we had gone the other way. The opposite to Doros. He was right behind us and right behind him was a crash of glass as the crowd spilled out onto the street to kill him.

Quick, jump in my van, jump in my van.

We jump in his bright orange Transit and he just about speeds away as a shower of beer bottles and pint glasses smash against the roof and back doors. He drives like a maniac for half a mile up the road to North Finchley bus garage (wherever that is) and when we get there he goes:

Right, Stelly, thanks for sticking your neck out. Shame it got

stabbed. You can get out, go home, you're injured.
Stelly didn't need to be told twice. He jumps out still crying about his neck but before I am able to jump out after him, Doros pulls away at speed and goes:
Jooks, you haven't got a scratch, apart from your bleeding arse. You're coming back with me to fight them.

THIRTY-THREE
And you let him drive you back to get your arse stabbed again?

FIFTEEN
I couldn't believe it. I look at Doros as if to say are you having a laugh, and there's this wild look of insanity in his eyes. You know, like Dracula. When I saw that, I took my life in my own hands and jumped out of the Transit as Doros does a turn. I went flying. Coulda killed meself.

SIXTEEN
Like one of them westerns.

FIFTY
That's not how Stelly remembers it. He says you left him for dead.

FIFTEEN
Fuck are you saying?

FIFTY
I bumped into him the other day. All random and all. In the middle of the night. In Wood Green of all places. In a kebab shop. You know that late night one that's been there since the days when the bingo hall next door was still the Odeon. Stelly is in there. I barely recognise him. My best friend in life and I mistake him for some random drunk. It's been more than twenty years and he's the worst for wear and he's now got a lot of chops about his chops. And he's ranting.
JOOKS, JOOKS, I don't believe it. I don't believe it.
The kebab shop is pack-out, you know. And everybody is looking up thinking there's about to be a ruck and, instead,

when I finally recognise him, we embrace like long-lost best friends who haven't seen each other for twenty years. Anyway, I've got to go, see, I've got a car full of people waiting on me. But before I go, Stelly says:

You nearly got me killed that time at The Orange Tree.

That wasn't me, that was FIFTEEN.

I haven't forgotten, JOOKS, how you were trying to impress on that girl, Judy, at The Grange and how you got all James Deany with her when Doros tells us to go with him to Friern Barnet to get our heads kicked in. You went over to her and said you had to go and it was a matter of honour and you told her that you would come back a hero. And she laughed and said, 'I'll be waiting'.

But you couldn't go back a hero, could you Jooks? Cos you knew what I knew and I knew that you knew that I knew that you knew I knew that you clucked all the way home that night. KFC. Without apology. Don't fuck around, Jooks, I caught your eye when I got stabbed as I was being kicked about the pub like a rag doll. You took one look at me and scarpered with a cue stick up your arse. Out the door. Left me for dead. That's why I got stabbed by that woman who was going around stabbing everybody. You remember her, don't you? You should have been watching out for me, Jooks. If you had had my back, she couldn't have stabbed me. And if you hadn't done a runner and left me, I would have had your back and you wouldn't have got 'stabbed' up the arse.

FIFTEEN
It wasn't like that. Behave. I would never leave my best mate for dead. Even if he was dead.

FIFTY
And it wasn't in the neck. I thought it was as well. Stelly said: *If I had got stabbed in the neck I'd be pushing up daisies, you prat. It was on the side of the head. Just behind my left ear. That's why I'm so hard of hearing in that ear.*

FIFTEEN
You calling me a liar? You want a fight about it?

FIFTY
Don't shoot the messenger. Stelly told me all about it. That

was the last time I spoke to him before he died.

FIFTEEN
Stelly is dead!

FIFTY
Yeah. Few months back. Didn't you know? Keeled over and died. Just like that. Gone.

FIFTEEN
My best friend.

TWENTY
Mine too.

FIFTY
Yeah, collapsed on the pavement at the top of Roseberry Gardens. Turns out he had the tip of a knife blade lodged in the side of his head. Just behind his left ear. All these years. And then it moved.

FIFTEEN
Shit.

FIFTY
Yeah, shit, you left Stelly to get stabbed. In his own words. And that's what eventually kills him.

FIFTEEN
Fuck off, wanker. I always get the blame. For everything.

FIFTY-THREE
Yeah, leave the kid alone. You can't put that on him and all.

TWENTY-THREE
Oi, jellyhead, how can you be a teddy boy? Ain't you never heard of Kelso Cochrane?

FIFTEEN
Don't call me that. What have I ever done to you?

FIFTY-TWO
Everything. Think where I would be today if it wasn't for all this time wasted getting into trouble?

FIFTEEN
What d'you want me to do, kill myself?

FIFTY-TWO
T-R-O-U-B-L-E. Mate, when are you going to learn that there are no privileges in life. You have to earn them. All you're earning at the moment is a good hiding.

FIFTY
So Stelly's death is now the subject of a murder enquiry. You see why someone might be trying to kill you. A witness.

FIFTY
I always thought it was a bloke who went round stabbing everybody in The Orange Tree.

THIRTY-THREE
Your imagination is getting as bad as JOOKS's.

FIFTEEN
And anyway I'm going to get my face smashed in tomorrow. Martinez is going to kick the shit out of me. He's a nutcase. I owe him ninety-five quid.

FIFTY-TWO
Ninety-five quid! That's like grands now. No way are you going to be able to pay him on 10 pence a week pocket money. Not in a month of Mondays. You are going to get the shit kicked out of you.

FIFTEEN
Yeah, we just kept playing double or quits. And he's the hardest man in school. That's how I got this black eye.

THIRTY-SEVEN
What black eye?

FORTY
It's a real shiner. I thought you were born that way.

FIFTEEN
I shouldn't have given him no lip.

FOURTEEN
Martinez will have your guts for garters. He mashed up
this prefect, twice his size, and drags his cheek across the
pavement like a brillo pad.

SEVENTEEN
Yeah, he gets sent down – murder. For life. Same age
as me. Did you know? Him and Everton White. Teenage
murderers. Went to rob Martinez's uncle and ended up
stabbing him.

FIFTEEN
Didn't I say he's a nutter. He must know I've got no way
of getting ninety-five quid by tomorrow.I'm still on 10p a
week pocket money. After all these years.

FIFTY-TWO
Yeah, you're definitely going to get more shit kicked out of
you than you've ever had in your life. He might even stab
you for fun. But at least you don't end up in the cemetery
like Martinez's uncle. Otherwise we wouldn't be here to
tell the tale.

FIFTEEN
Ollie's going to bring some of his bad boys from Highgate
Wood over to Stationers' tomorrow morning to come and
show Martinez what's what. That should teach him.

FIFTY
I love the guy. Ollie would do anything for his kid bro.

FIFTY-TWO
More trouble. You're not keeping it real out here. Can't you see
how foolish you are? Borrow my eyes. See things the way

they really are. You're just another kid from the hood with nothing much going for you. Stick to the frigging script.

EIGHTEEN
Remember I got bottled the other day cos of Stelly. At some bring a bottle party above the old Salisbury pub on the corner of Green Lanes and St Ann's Road in the N4s.

JOOKS
That's about the only landmark left standing in the ends.

EIGHTEEN
Minding my own business. In the ends for one night only. First time in ages. Getting my thing going with some girl when Stelly comes all mad and screwing about some guy who wants a ruck. Everybody round our way knows if you start a ruck with Stelly you start a ruck with me and vice versa. The moment I saw it was a black guy, I didn't want no ruck. I don't want to have to choose between a best friend and a brother. I can't pick sides. But I don't get a chance to broker peace neither. The moment I step into the room the guy is like, *Oh you want a ruck too* and, before I can say no, he whacks me over the head with his bring a beer bottle. Coulda killed me. Killed the party for me. But the girl felt sorry for me so she followed me home to make sure I was all right. Which was all right as it goes.

FIFTY-TWO
Goodness sake. Control your libido. Else we're all screwed.

JOOKS
Could she be the one who is trying to murder me? TEN, NINE... what were you saying about ghosts?

NINE
A tiny little baby. And she keeps crying and crying but there ain't no tears cos she ain't got no eyes.

JOOKS
How can you dream such dreams? What's the matter with you?

Kid your age shouldn't be having nightmares like that.

NINE
It's not a dream.

JOOKS
But it's not real, right? So it's got to be a dream.

TEN
It really is real.

JOOKS
If you say it's real, it's real. It's real to you is all that matters.
How come no one else has a memory of this?

TEN
Cos I wiped it out. I had to. It's so horrible. After what happened
to EIGHT I had to wipe it out. For everybody's sake.

JOOKS
How do you wipe out a memory? And what happened to
EIGHT?

TEN
Well, I had to spin round and round clockwise until I got
dizzy and the whole world was spinning and spinning and
spinning the other way round and I fell to the ground and
banged my head really hard on the ground and when I
woke up I couldn't remember anything about it.

JOOKS
What?! That's mad. How come you've remembered now?

TEN
Well, I spun round and round the other way round until I
got dizzy and the whole world was spinning and I fell to
the ground and banged my head really hard on the ground
and when I woke up I remembered again.

JOOKS
And what happened to EIGHT? Why won't you tell me?

TEN
Cos I don't know. I can't remember. He must have spun round and round and round clockwise until it was wiped. For all our sakes.He's the only one who can unwipe from his memory.

SIXTY
None of us knows.

TWENTY-FIVE

He never really returned from the wars.

JOOKS
What happened, EIGHT? What happened to make you so wotless?

EIGHT

Ee-aye-addi-o I'm not a fucking grass

JOOKS
You really believe you can unwipe memory by spinning round?

TWENTY-FIVE
Descartes reckons he did it.

EIGHT

Oranges and lemons say the bells of St Clement...

TWENTY-SIX
I've got this memory from Lagos that's been niggling at the back of my mind for ages and it pops up sometimes. I don't know the details, but there was some woman at the hospital with her baby sitting on the long benches in the shade of an outdoor waiting area, in the days when women in Nigeria would wrap up their money in a handkerchief and then hold it in the wraps of their shawl around their

waist, and you saw her handkerchief full of money drop from the folds of her wrapper and you didn't say a word.

SIX
Please don't say anything. Please. Papa will be so angry.

TWENTY-SIX
He'll wallop you sadly cos it was the opposite of what he would do. When we first came here and we were so broke he didn't know where he was going to find the money to buy food to feed his children one day. He was standing in a queue at the post office and the guy ahead of him in the line drops his wallet without knowing it and it crossed the old man's mind... but he bent down, picked up the wallet and handed it to the man, to the man's relief. We went hungry that night but the old man was righteous. Say what you like about him.

SIX
I wanted to give the woman her money but I wanted sweets.

FORTY
I still think of that woman. I still feel guilty. She was crying that she had lost her money and couldn't afford to pay the doctor to treat her baby. She looked everywhere, under the bench and everything and you didn't say a word.

THIRTY
Cold. If they had searched you and found the handkerchief they would have flogged you to within an inch of your life and then they would have shaved off all your hair and rubbed enough oil on your head for the sun to shine on it wherever you went to alert everybody that you are a thief. They did that to all the kids caught with their hands in the cookie jar. You're lucky they didn't catch you, you thieving bastard.

SIX
I did not see her cry. I went to the toilet in the hospital to look at the money. It was Cousin Chooks told me she was crying. By then she was gone. Please don't tell my father.

FORTY
You're going hell. Original sin. I wonder how important that money was to her? Whether she was able to eat that day and feed her child and if she was able to pay the doctor while you bought sweets with her money.

FORTY
That's where it all started.

FIFTY
Original sin.

FORTY
That's why we're in this mess.

JOOKS
Lucky for you the old man is dead so he will never know, SIX.

FIFTEEN
Daddy... dead?

JOOKS
Yeah, the old man... dead. I have a confession to make...

EFFRIES

DON'T TELL ME, YOU MURDERED YOUR OLD MAN. DO YOU NOT READ YOUR HEBREW BIBLE? HONOUR THY FATHER AND THY MOTHER. HOW HARD CAN THAT BE? SO THAT YOUR DAYS MAY BE LONGER.

This is real. It's not the Old Testament. It's not que sera sera. It's not prophecy. Things could have turned out differently but they didn't. I had to make a choice.

OYF SIMCHES, MY FRIEND. LIFE'S A MOTHERFUCKER.

There you are going on about the ancient greeks and the father of psychopathology again. Please stop calling me a mother fucker. Call it a complex if you like but don't fuck around with my mum. I'll kill a man for that.

YOU WRETCH YOU. KILL A MAN OVER A WOMAN, THAT'S LIFE. LIFE'S A CRIME OF PASSION. KILL A WOMAN OVER A MAN, THAT'S FUCKRIES. THAT'S FUCKED UP. IF YOU MURDER YOUR FATHER. YOU ARE CURSED FOREVER. IF YOU THEN HAVE IT OFF WITH YOUR MUM YOU MAY AS WELL GET A SPOON AND SCOOP OUT YOUR EYEBALLS. CAN'T YOU SEE?

You were the one accusing me of not having a conscience? It appears you're the one who doesn't know how to spell it.

WHICH ONE OF YOU IS THE REAL YOU?

What does it matter? The me that matters is the one who pulled the trigger.

IN WHICH CASE LET ME SAVE YOU FROM YOURSELF. I USED TO BE A RASTA MAN, REMEMBER?

JOOKS
The old man didn't just die, he was murdered.

FIFTEEN
Say it's not true.

FORTY
Murdered? The old man?

JOOKS
Yes. The old man. Still call him 'sir'. After all these years.
To sir with love. I was there when he was murdered.

TWENTY-FIVE
Don't tell me... you killed him?

THIRTY-THREE
Good question.

FIFTEEN
Say it's not true. Daddy forgive me. For everything. I'm sorry
daddy. I love you. I'm going to miss you. Don't leave me.

JOOKS
I thought you would be delighted he was dead. Weren't you
planning on killing him?

FIFTEEN
Why would I kill my dad? Are you mad? He's my dad.

JOOKS
But what about the beating you took last night? What about
your flick knife? What about your broken finger?

FIFTEEN
I'll live with that. We're all going to live with that. It's
only a broken finger. Doesn't mean I want my dad dead.
Are you mad?

FIFTY
The old man murdered. Unbelievable.

JOOKS
I feel so guilty.

THIRTY-THREE
Finally. A confession. So you're the murderer you've been looking for all along. How can you not have known that you are the you wot done it? The you you've been looking for. Why were you trying to blame us?

JOOKS
I can see what you're trying to do. You've never liked me. For your information Misstra 'Know-It-All', it was the doctor who actually murdered him. Not me. I only gave the orders.

THIRTY-THREE
And that's your defence, is it, 'I was only giving orders'. You think that will go down in Nuremberg?

TEN
Aren't doctors supposed to keep you alive?

JOOKS
He made out like the morphine would ease his discomfort not hasten his death. I said 'Cool' and they gave him a shot. A moment later he was gone.

THIRTY-THREE
So it was you?

JOOKS
But I didn't know I was killing him.

THIRTY-THREE
Murderer.

JOOKS
Leave it out. I gave the nod. I'm not the murderer.

THIRTY-THREE
I can't wait to hear how you work that out.

SIXTY
How do you live with yourself?

JOOKS
Hear me out. The old man was in a bad way. No doubt. Unconscious. Struggling to breathe. All sorts of tubes down him. They said the opium would relieve his discomfort. I believed them. Blossom knew what was what though. She kept saying it would hasten his death. I didn't know what she meant. I thought she meant that instead of living another ten years he might only live another seven years. All I wanted was to ease his pain. We are all asthmatics. Struggling to breathe ain't no joke. Every breath was like his last. I did what anyone of us would have done under the circumstances. He didn't stand a chance.

THIRTY-THREE
In a court of law you're going down for murder. First degree. No way round it. You're as guilty as that bloke they hanged when he said 'Let him have it'.

THIRTY-FOUR
Derek Bentley.

THIRTY-THREE
The brutality. The inhumanity. How old was he? Eighty? A defenceless eighty year old. How could you?

JOOKS
You've got a cheek.

FIFTEEN
How could you? Didn't I tell you that he told me that under no circumstances was I to switch off his life support if he was in hospital unconscious. I was to keep him alive no matter what. Those were his orders. I passed that on to pass it on.

EFFRIES

SIXTEEN
I did.

NINETEEN
I did too.

SIXTY
Me too.

THIRTY-THREE
We were supposed to be his life support. And you went and killed him when he was out of it. That's like shooting a man in the back. What are you, Billy The Kid?

JOOKS
It's not every day you get to make a life or death decision. I called it wrong. That's my only crime.

THIRTY-THREE
I still reckon it's murder though. You had us all on a wild goose chase when you knew all along what was really going on. I'd call that obstructing the course of justice.

JOOKS
How's the old man's death connected to my murder me?

EIGHT
Daddy dead-o.

FIFTY-NINE
Kinda weird talking about him in the past tense.

SIXTY
Sometimes you've got to draw a line and forget the past.

TWENTY-SIX
Too many regrets. Doesn't bear thinking about.

FORTY
The amount of forgetting we've had to do.

SIXTY
I sat with him for hours that last year and watched him disappear into the distance. Close up and personal. He couldn't say anything. About the good times or the bad times.

THIRTEEN
Loads of bad times.

SIXTEEN
Some good times too.

TWENTY-TWO
Loads of time.

FORTY-TWO
That's what we ain't got in this bitch of a life.

SIXTY
He wouldn't speak to you if you didn't have a degree. Remember?

FORTY-TWO
He loved his kids. Especially when we were little. He showed a lot of tenderness back then before the stress of bringing us over. The easier option would have been to leave us in Nigeria. England is the bitch that screwed him.

FIFTY-THREE
Remember the solution to solving quadratic equations: $x = -b \pm \sqrt{(b2 - 4ac)} \, 2a$ He taught us that when we were SEVEN.

SEVEN
Y-yes. X equals m-minus Buh-B plus or m-minus the s-square r-root of Buh-B s-squared all over t-two A.

FIFTY-FIVE
Wot good has that done you?

FIFTY-THREE
That's not the point. That's the old man. A real original.

EFFRIES

FOURTEEN
If he is so clever how come we live in the ends?

FIFTY-THREE
Tottenham's only part of the story.

THIRTY
Did someone say *paaaaaarty!*

FIFTY-FIVE
He used to talk for England on the phone on a Sunday with Uncle K. Remember? Non-stop. All day long. An immigrant's story, yeah. Two brothers, both alike in dignity, one in north and one in south - London, in the days before mobiles when phone calls cost a bomb. They would talk all day. Joke was they would talk at the same time. Simultaneously. Neither of them heard a word the other was saying for hours.

TWELVE
I got an audition to Opportunity Knocks with Hughie Green. The old man took me to the audition at Teddington Lock. I didn't get through but he was like:
Well done, you performed like a pro. You never know, today Tottenham, tomorrow Hollywood.

NINE
That's what he said when I was in The Oblong Box an' all.

SIXTY
The Oblong Box, eh? Hammer House of Horror starring Vincent Price and Christopher Lee... and EIGHT. I talk about it all the time.

JOOKSY
Someone's clipped EIGHT's bit and put it online. Go to YouTube and type in 'Oblong Box' and 'Mike' together and you'll see it. 34 seconds of stardom.

TWELVE
When I went up to Pinewood Studios to be in Diamonds Are

EFFRIES

Forever it was *Today Tottenham, tomorrow Hollywood.* But then when Hollywood came for me the old man said 'No'. He wasn't allowing his son to be no slave in no movie.

TWENTY
Wish I had listened. Always. He was right. I did get myself in a lot of trouble. Just like he said I would if I carried on like I was carrying on.

TWENTY-FIVE
Remember that time you challenged him to a race, TEN? When you lot thought you were faster. You thought you could beat him, remember? And he bet you your 10 pence a week pocket money against a tenner if he lost. And he invited the whole gang to join in the challenge – Ollie, Nicholas, Alex, the Tanners and Greek George. And we went across to the cricket field in the park down by the Green Lanes end.

FIFTY-SEVEN
Oh, that's a baseball field now. Drive past it all the time.

TWENTY-FIVE
None of you primary school pupils stood a chance against a grown man over 100 metres and the old man wasn't ramping. He ran like his life depended upon it. Against ten year olds.

TWENTY-TWO
Wish I had listened to him too. Make a plan before going to university, he said. A plan of what you are going there for and how you are going to achieve it. However difficult that might be. A plan to stick to.

JOOKS
If only I could dance with my father again.

FIFTY-NINE
He would say:
You still not PM yet? You've got a degree haven't you? The PM doesn't have any more than that. Why aren't you prime minister?

102

FORTY-SEVEN
He couldn't take the humiliation of his sons not winning in everything.

FORTY-EIGHT
Life is a two-horse race, as far as he is concerned. Coming second is coming last.

JOOKS
Extremely emotional experiences leave traces in memory that cannot be extinguished, I guess.

THIRTY-THREE
Fucksake. I had a feeling today was going to be one of them extremely emotional experiences days. Fucksake.

JOOKS
What was that?

THIRTY-THREE
Nothing. Just running off at the mouth as usual. Moaning.

JOOKS
Sorry. I wasn't listening.

THIRTY-THREE
I'm not listening to you either. I'm deep in thought.

EIGHT
There was an old lady of ninety-two
Parlez-vous...
Done a fart and let it roll
Inky pinky parlez-vous

JOOKS
The intensity of an experience is not a sufficient safeguard against forgetting.

THIRTY-THREE
Where'd you get this mumbo-jumbo?

EFFRIES

NINETEEN
Say that again.

THIRTY-ONE
The old man, eh? I remember when it wasn't so sad.

SEVENTEEN
Chucked me out. Packed my bags and threw me out. I'm not crying him a river. Maybe when I'm older but not right now.

EIGHTEEN
Mate, it wasn't quite like that, you're re-writing history. He didn't chuck you out, he gave you a choice. Books or disco. You chose disco. So you had to go. His house, his rules.

FIFTY-NINE
With the benefit of hindsight the studying has made a difference. For the family. How many dads had five sons at university all at the same time? Stands out. Ahead of his time.

NINE
Wish things were the way they were before we came here.

TEN
How much do you really remember about back then?

FIFTY-SIX
Don't know if you lot realise but on September 19th it will be fifty years exactly since me and Ollie arrived on these shores from Nigeria. Half a century. Can you believe it? I remember sitting on a BOAC plane, at the back of the cabin in my school uniform, being looked after by cabin crew.

FIFTY-SEVEN
I don't have a memory of arriving in London, but I do recall the bedsit in Hornsey. The room which me and Ollie would share with only a curtain to save our parents' modesty.

SIX
I want to go back to Nigeria. I want to go home.

FIFTY-SEVEN
Then we were homeless. It was student digs and the landlord did not allow children. So we got thrown out. Remember, these were No Blacks, No Irish, No Dogs days. A young black family trying to get somewhere to live... wasn't easy. So the old man had to pay a premium for a one bedroom in Golders Green.

FIFTY-EIGHT
Half a century. Surely by now I should feel British. And yet I'm like a stranger in my own country.

SIXTY
Hard to feel British when you're having jollof for tea.

EIGHT
My old man's a dustman
He wears a dustman's hat...

TWENTY-SEVEN
The old man would go ballistic if he heard that. After all the time he spent getting a PhD he would take it as a personal diss that you would even joke that he's a dustman.

SIX
Where's my mummy, sah? What happened to her?

EIGHTEEN
She left Lagos and moved to Benin City to begin a new life away from the scene of her sadness. She agreed to let you and Ollie go. For better or worse.

SIXTY
At such a young age.

THIRTY-EIGHT
Coming to England was like 'opportunity knocks' for us. She accepted that. Too much too young she couldn't imagine her children would call another woman 'mum'.

EIGHTEEN
She was heartbroken not having her children around her. And that was it for the next twelve years. For Ollie it was forever. He never saw his mum again.

THIRTY-ONE
The old man can't have been thinking straight. That's what gets me. Children need their mums.

FORTY-NINE
It's only been 25 years. You'll get over it. Believe. Passage of time and all that. Wait until it's 40 years and counting.

SEVEN
You m-m-murdered my father.

JOOKS
Look, kid, I keep saying it wasn't like that. Please don't make it worse for me. It's not my fault. Do you think I would have given the doctor the okay to administer the injection if I had known the drugs were going to kill him? It was a tough, tough call. I feel guilty, I really do. I regret what I did. I'm going to have to live with it. Tough luck. Just tough. But not murder. Not my part in it.

THIRTY-THREE
Tough luck? You live, he dies.

FIFTIES
The older you get the more regrets you carry. You end up bearing everybody's regrets. Biggest regret must be not staying in Nigeria. On account of how mum dies.

SIX
Mummy is dead?

FOURTEEN
But she left for work the same time I left for school. I walked up the road with her. She wasn't even ill.

EFFRIES

TWENTY-EIGHT
Passed away a couple months back. In the summer. Asthma attack. Fifty-one. Can you believe it?

SEVENTEEN
Oh gosh, oh no. Mummy dead?

TWENTY-EIGHT
Yeah, sorry to break it to you. The olders know.

SEVENTEEN
No, no, no, no.

SIXTEEN
Mummy, dead?

NINE
This is getting really scary. All the people we know are dead. That's loads of ghosts.

FIFTIES
You know you've got another mother. Mummy's your step-mum. You know, yeah?

EIGHTEEN
Only just met her. Back in Nigeria. First time in years.

SIX
So mummy's not dead?

THIRTEEN
I have one memory of her. I don't know whether it is real.

EIGHTEEN
She shows up one night and asks: *Do you know who I am?* How was I to remember? Broke her heart that I didn't know.

FORTIES
Why don't you stay there, in Nigeria, in Benin City?

107

EFFRIES

EIGHTEEN
Business reasons.

SIXTEEN
Cos of some girl, innit?

SEVENTEEN
It's always cos of some girl.

FIFTY-SEVEN
Girls come, girls go. That's why all our friends are divorcing.

EIGHTEEN
Do you have any idea what it's like to be young, free and single in this permissive society? Have you forgotten?

NINETEEN
Just stay there, man. With your mum. You get to be with her for the first time in nearly thirteen years. You can't abandon her after only a few weeks.

EIGHTEEN
It's been a couple of months.

NINETEEN
Which is fine, if she doesn't die six months later. If she does, these couple of months are precious moments in a lifetime. If you leave her you leave me to pick up the pieces.

EIGHTEEN
If, if, if. There's a lot of 'ifs' there.

FIFTIES
You're throwing away the chance to spend every day with your mum. You're having a laugh.

EIGHTEEN
At least I'm here. Of my own initiative. I don't see you around. First opportunity I had. I'm here collecting memories for you. All of you. And it's not just any girl. It's my girl. I'm in love

EFFRIES

FIFTIES
Love. What do you know about love?

EIGHTEEN
You don't have to be a fool to fall in love. I'm crazy about the girl. Can't eat, can't sleep. Just to be with her.

NINETEEN
Yeah, I remember, that's the way it was.

THIRTIES
Haha, you call that love? Be real. Don't act like it's a biggie, just go about your business like it's any other day.

FIFTIES
Was? NINETEEN said 'was'. So it's over. You abandon our mum for some girl you're not even together with forever?

EIGHTEEN
You've been in love haven't you? What happens happens.

FIFTIES
Not the point. We're talking mummy. Love cools. Give it time.

FIFTY-ONE
So you're going ahead. You've made your decision and now you're making our bed. You're making our decision for us.

JOOKS
Love makes you lose your mind. Sometimes it's like that. Real love is right there under your nose but you don't see it. Because this other thing called 'love' is messing with you.

THIRTY-THREE
More mumbo-jumbo.

THIRTY-SIX
Tell me about it. The last place I expected to find it was under my nose. But there it was. All the time.

EFFRIES

TWENTIES
Should have been me.

JOOKS
I'm talking a mother's love. Right under my nose.

THIRTIES
Yeah, should have been. She was right there in the palm of your hands. Under your nose. But you couldn't see it. I'm talking the love of a woman you want to sleep with.

SIXTY
Seek and you won't find Ms Right if you're looking to get laid.

THIRTY-THREE
Fucksake. Is it going to be like this all night long?

THIRTY
What about Bill Haley, eh, in Stevenage. At the Mecca. How many people can say they saw him live. Kiss curl an' all.

TWELVE
Amazing. Back to the fifties. The look on his face when he saw the only black face in the place was like, *What... the...*

FOURTEEN
It was more like *What? The...?* when he saw me. He wasn't all that. On reflection, definitely not amazing. He must have gone through them ropes ten thousand times before.

JOOKS
How did you end up in a police cell?

TWELVE
Got lost in the fifties and missed the last train home.

TWENTYSOMETHINGS
In Stevenage? You idiot. How are you going to get home? You've got to get home before the old man finds out you're not home. He'll kill you. You idiot.

FOURTEEN
Oi, talk to TWELVE like that but I'm not having it. What was I supposed to do? Ol' Bill kept coming back for encores. I couldn't leave could I?

TWELVE
I'm only fucking TWELVE. Lay off me. I missed the train. Big deal.

FOURTEEN
You weren't even there.

JOOKS
Which one of you was it? TWELVE? FOURTEEN? And again, how did you end up in a police cell?

FOURTEEN
You know my mouth.

TWELVE
My gob's bigger.

FOURTEEN
When I missed the train at Stevenage, I started hitch-hiking. I'd never done it before. It was dark and scary. Got a lift to Welwyn Garden City and couldn't get any further. It was 2 o'clock in the morning. I found a cop shop. As I go in the officer at the front desk goes:
What do you want?
I could tell he wasn't having it but I had no way of getting home if ol' bill refused to run a taxi service for me.
Not tonight, sunshine, he goes. *Now fuck off out of it.*

TWELVE
So I started crying. Bawling my eyes out. On purpose. For a bed and blanket. Another cop comes out to see what all the wailing is about. He wants to know where I live and my home number to call up the old man to come and get me.
No, you don't understand, my old man's not like that.
The cop goes:

EFFRIES

He's going to have to be like that cos you're only twelve.

FOURTEEN
Fourteen.

TWELVE
Twelve year olds can't be walking the streets on their own in the middle of the night, he goes.

FOURTEEN
NEVER TELL THE COPS THE TRUTH is what the olders in the ends say. So I give them Stelly's number. His old man will sleep through an earthquake. That phone will be ringing all night long and nobody will answer. Anyway, they must have been trying to call Stelly's for ages. I'm sitting there, in the station, when the good cop comes across and jabs me in the eye.
Aaaaargh! I'M BLIND, I'M BLIND, I'M BLIND. AARRGGHH.
I was screaming my head off, too afraid to look in case he had jabbed my eye so hard I was cross-eyed.
Think you're a smartarse making a fool out of me.
Like I said, nobody answered the phone at Stelly's. So ol' bill go round there, to Roseberry Gardens, from the nearby nick.

FIFTY-EIGHT
Not a nick no more. It's been gentrified into a block of flats that only people who aren't from round here can afford.

FOURTEEN
Stelly's old man finally wakes up and comes down the stairs and opens the door to see the ol' bill on his doorstep.
We've got your son down Welwyn Garden nick.
No you haven't, Stelly's old man goes.
And the ol' bill tells him, *Yes we have.*
And Stelly's old man goes up to Stelly's bedroom to see him sleeping soundly in his bed. The Tottenham cops relay that to Welwyn and now good cop's got the hump cos I made him look as thick as two planks and he's now threatening to jook me in the other eye so it matches the cross-eyed one. With only one straight eye left I had to tell

him the truth. And he calls up the old man and when he comes back he says:

Right, I've spoken to your old man and when I asked him what he wants us to do with you, he goes, 'Do whatever you want with him.' That's your old man saying that. So behave or you'll be walking out of here on crutches.

And he locks me in a cell for the night.

JOOKS
How old are you?

TWELVE
Twelve.

JOOKS
Is that even legal?

FIFTY
He made a lot of mistakes, the old man, not least in the discipline department. But he isn't a bad man at heart.

FIFTEEN
Sometimes, some days, he breaks my spirit.

FIFTY
Yeah, well, YEAH. His spirit is broken too.

SIXTY
Was. His spirit *was* broken.

FIFTY-NINE
The old man… was a don. When all is said and done.

SIXTY
Man of iron. Mighty lion.

FORTY-TWO
No idea who his sons are. As smart as he is he doesn't have a clue. About me, about you, about us and what we get up to.

SIXTY
If only he could see us today, eh?

FORTY-TWO
Reckon he could handle it? Seeing who we really are.

FIFTY-ONE
Course he could. He handled FIFTEEN making a fool of his teddy boy self. He could handle anything.

TWENTY-SIX
Yeah, England is a bitch.

THIRTY-NINE
Never mind England, what happened to top of the class? That's all he ever wanted. We broke his spirit.

TEN
What are you looking at me for?

TWELVE
I wouldn't have got into a lot of this shit if it wasn't for you? I used to be top of the class.

TEN
Why you blaming me? I'm not stopping you.

THIRTY-NINE
Whatever you're doing – moving with the wrong crowd, running with the bad bwoys – don't. Stick with the geeks. Moretti in your class is going to Cambridge. Hang with him.

THIRTY-THREE
Jeez. Talk about a zoo.

JOOKS
What?

THIRTY-THREE
This. How can you have your thirty-nine year old telling

your twelve year old to hang out with the kids who get slapped around by the other kids for not being normal, in lieu of some moral reward some time in the distant future?

FIFTY-EIGHT
But they're the masters of the universe. The school geeks are the ones who run things now. They're having the last laugh with the world's most beautiful women.

JOOKS
Top of the class. England. Six year olds in Nigeria today would see that as the winning ticket in the lottery of life, right in the palm of your hands. Then you go and lose it.

SIX
Sah, I did not want to come. So far from home, I cried for days. I want to go back. I cried for a week. *I want to go back.* My father bought me a cowboy suit. I still cried. The next day he bought me a cowboy hat and rifle. I am still crying.

SEVENTEEN
I can't remember my own mother. She must have gone to the airport to wave us goodbye when we left but I don't remember. And there are no photographs of her at home.

EIGHT
Black girl in the ring tra la la la lee...

JOOKS
It's a *brown* girl in the ring. Don't sing it. It's creepy. A slave owner selling his own daughter at auction. Disgusting shit.

TWENTY-ONE
Man to man is so unjust.

JOOKS
Ping! Oh no, another voicemail:

JOOKS, THE WAIT IS NEARLY OVER. MIDNIGHT, YEAH?

GREETINGS IN THE NAME OF OUR LORD AND SAVIOUR WHO HAS THIS DAY REVEALED HIMSELF IN THE PERSONALITY OF HIS IMPERIAL MAJESTY EMPEROR HAILE SELASSIE I. KING OF KINGS, LORD OF LORDS, CONQUERING LION OF THE TRIBE OF JUDAH, HIGH ELECT OF GOD, EVER LIVING GOD, EARTH'S RIGHTFUL RULER – *RASTAFARI!*
GREETINGS THROUGH THE TWELVE TRIBES OF ISRAEL, WHICH WAS LOST AND SCATTERED ABROAD NOW FOUNDED IN JAMAICA BY OUR BELOVED PROPHET, DR VERNON CARRINGTON GAD 1ST.
GREETINGS THROUGH THE ORTHODOX FAITH WHICH IS NOT ONE OF WRITS NOR RITES BUT A TRUE FUNCTION OF THE HEART, ACQUIRED THROUGH A NATURALLY MYSTICAL INCORPORATION, IN PLAIN WORDS BORN AGAIN.
GREETINGS THROUGH THE ROYAL HOUSE OF DAVID, NAMELY OUR CROWN PRINCE, ZARA YACOB ASFA WOSSEN AHMA SELASSIE. MAY THE MOST HIGH ELOHIM OF ISRAEL BE WITH YOU WITH HIS HOLY RIGHTEOUSNESS.

You are doing my head in. I ain't got time for this. Midnight is fast approaching. I could be dead soon.

LET THE DEAD BURY THE DEAD.

That's too technical.

HEAR THIS, MAN. EVERYT'ING IS EVERYT'ING. SEEN?

I could do with a little everything's gonna be all right at midnight.

YOU'RE COMING LIKE A BOB MARLEY SONG. LEARN THIS, EVEN IF YOUR SIN IS AS SMALL AS A MUSTARD SEED YOU DON'T GET TO HEAVEN TO DRINK MILK AND HONEY.

You take man's breath away. I swear.

THE DEVIL IS A DANGEROUS GUY. SEEN?

FOURTH LOAD

NINETEEN

So here I am on the Trans Euro Express from Amsterdam to Stockholm. So glad to be out of 'Nam, I can't tell you, in one of those compartments for eight with a gangway along the side and these two Swedish guys, about my age, come in with their backpacks and they're telling me about their journey up from Morocco. Three days it's taken them without a bite to eat. I tell 'em that I'm hungry too. Then this Yank with a beard joins us in Osnabrück and he's got a bottle of vodka, see, and the Swedes grab it off him cos they're starving, and guzzle it all down like camels at the oasis. I don't touch none of it. You know me. Neither does the yank. So the Swedes just drink and drink and drink to Lily the Pink until there's nothing left to drink. The bottle empty, the vodka is doing their talking, louder and louder and louder, and singing their heads off.

Tragedy
When you need the loo
And it won't come through
It's tragedy.
Diarrhoea
When your bum
Becomes a scatter gun
Diarrhoea

By the time we get to Copenhagen the Swedes can barely stand so they're lying on the floor. One of them has got a wet patch on his jeans and the other one has thrown up over himself. The yank is so relieved to be saying his goodbyes he leaves his hat and coat behind. Before I even get a chance to distance myself from the drunken duo a couple of border cops step into the compartment demanding passports. The Swedes start screaming *FASCIST PIGS! FASCIST PIGS! FASCIST PIGS!* and giving the cops the finger, so the cops decide to make them pay, make us all pay, by being the fascist pigs that they were being labelled.
STRIP. THE LOT OF YOU.
But I'm not with them.
ALL I WANT TO SEE IS ARSES AND ELBOWS.

EFFRIES

That ain't fair. Why should I have to strip and bend over?
ALL I WANT TO SEE IS ARSES AND ELBOWS.
Oh no. I just remembered, I'm carrying. Oh no. This ain't
really happening, I must be dreaming. I've got one foot in
smuggling jail. I'm shitting myself. I strip. Slowly.
TROUSERS.
You cannot be serious. Strip to my undies on a train? But I love cops.
You're not pigs to me. I wouldn't dream of calling you fascist pigs.
My mind's ticking a million miles a MINUTE.
TROUSERS.
Quick thinking. I pull my trousers down cos I'm not wearing
underpants and, stark bollock naked from the waist down, I
squat right there in the centre of the compartment and do a
dump. A proper stinker. I've never told you lot this, have I?

FORTY-TWO
No. For shame. Have you no shame?

NINETEEN
You should have seen the look on those border guards'
faces. They couldn't wait to get out of there fast enough.

FORTY-TWO
You are disgusting.

NINETEEN
What am I supposed to do when I'm shitting myself?

JOOKS
You lost your mind. What are you carrying?

NINETEEN
Blues. A handful. I totally forgot. My pockets are stuffed.

JOOKS
You're pushing your luck.

SIXTY
Give the yadda-yadda-yadda a rest. You're not even catholic.

JOOKS
Yadda-yadda-yadda? You're talking Class A. Why are we even arguing about this? What difference does it make?

NINETEEN
Hear me out, things are just about to get nasty.

TWENTY-ONE
When did you punks start getting into smack? From speed to smack. That's when it stopped being punk.

FIFTY-NINE
And crack. Plop-Plops is still on it. See the state of him.

JOOKS
Plop-Plops? For real? What kind of a person is called Plop-Plops?

NINETEEN
I know. I thought I knew but now I know I don't.

SIXTY
What about the shame and scandal in the family if you got caught smuggling? Did you not think of that?

NINETEEN
Not until Copenhagen.

TWENTY-TWO
You've got some bottle kid.

TWENTY-TWO
Moments make all the difference.

THIRTY-THREE
Knowing JOOKS, you'll want to go to the cops and own up.

TWENTY-ONE
Better not, y'know. I ain't going jail for that.

JOOKS
Remind me, how you end up in the laplander of luxury.

EIGHTEEN
Land of opportunity. London's a shit hole. Sweden's boring but they don't hate black as much. Not all of them.

SEVENTEEN
As long as you lose this virginity. Some girl's involved, yeah?

TWENTY-SEVEN
Always some girl involved otherwise what's the point?

NINETEEN
You little virgin. Wrapped around her little finger.

TWENTY-TWENTY
All summer.

JOOKS
We calling this a thing? We calling it a fling?

NINETEEN
Call it affairs of the heart. It loves you and leaves you.

TWENTY-SIX
Give it a rest, for fuck sake. Give your dick a rest.

SEVENTEEN
A golden opportunity if you're from the ends. I can't wait.

NINETEEN
Then she wants to kill you.

JOOKS
Is she still out there trying to kill you?

FORTY
What do you expect when you fall in love without hesitation?

EFFRIES

JOOKS
Trying to kill me.

THIRTY-THREE
Are you man or are you pussy?

NINETEEN
I still love her. More now than ever.

THIRTY-THREE
Come home. Somebody send the boy home. Put him on a plane, a train, a bus or a boat. He's fucked. Weeping over some woman. In front of us. I'm even embarrassed for you.

EIGHTEEN
What about my girl?

THIRTY-THREE
Are you mad? Have you not heard what I've just said?

EIGHTEEN
What about my heart?

THIRTY-THREE
Bring the boy home.

SEVENTEEN
No. Stay where you are. It's better than being here. In case you've forgotten, here is not just a shit hole, it's a shit sandwich without the bread. Enjoy your little holiday, bro.

EIGHTEEN
Me too. I'm crazy about the girl.

FIFTY
Yeah. Unfortunate circumstances though. To be in love.

EIGHTEEN
What unfortunate circumstances?

FIFTY
Uh-uh, never mind.

EIGHTEEN
Nah, man, what unfortunate circumstances?

FIFTY
Mate, the most unfortunate circumstances.

EIGHTEEN
Yeah, but what?

FIFTY
Mummy.

EIGHTEEN
She's a tuffy, you know mum. I said I would be back and I will be. Soon. Sooner than you think.

NINETEEN
You've got six months. Six months to be with her and you're swanning off to the Arctic.

EIGHTEEN
Six months? Where d'you get that from?

NINETEEN
Where d'you think?

EIGHTEEN
Mate, you're not writing my story. I am. I said I'll be back and I will be. Not that I deserve a medal, I'll come back and look after her. In a week or two. Got some stuff to sort out.

NINETEEN
It is Maria, isn't it? We haven't all got short memories.

EIGHTEEN
Okay, yes. You know what being in love is like.

NINETEEN
Yeah, but your mum comes first, man. As much as I love
Maria, mum comes first.

EIGHTEEN
Don't you think I know that. I'll be gone a month. Tops.
Two at the most.

NINETEEN
You selfish cunt. Can't you hear what I'm saying. Can't
you see you're robbing me of memories with my mum? For
crying out loud, I'm telling you, stay where you are. She
dies, guess who gets the telegram?

EIGHTEEN
Oh shit.

NINETEEN
Yes, oh shit. Shoulda been me.

TWENTY-FIVE
Nothing you can do about it.

THIRTY-THREE
Like hell there isn't. You need to stay with her. In Nigeria.
You need to stay where you are. Look after her.

EIGHTEEN
I've already bought the ticket. Maria's expecting me. In Sweden.

SIXTY
If you get on that plane it will break her heart. You'll say
you'll be back but you'll never see her again. It's never
going to mend... that broken heart of hers.

NINETEEN
She won't survive another broken heart.

EIGHTEEN
Okay. Gimme time. I'll figure something out. You need to

stop speeding though. All that sulphate is turning your mind to mush.

NINETEEN
It's nor the sulphate it's the weed. I'm no grass. Nearly landed me behind bars. I shouldn't even have been there. Halfway down Götgatan just past Medborgarplatsen. Moses pulls up in this racing green Beetle with a Rolls Royce grill, and goes:
JOOKS, I'm flying to the moon, you coming?

SIXTY
Say no. Say no. Can't you see, he's off his head.

NINETEEN
Behind him in the back seat in wraparound shades is Simba, this skinny dude with baby locks, one of the bad bwoys from the Gambian mafia. The whole car stinks of weed.

SIXTY
Don't get in. Get in that car and the cops pull you over, it's over. A fatal error of judgement. Mess us all up.

NINETEEN
You're right. I shouldn't have got in.

SIXTY
What did I just tell you? Moses is as high as a hot air balloon and that is a lot of weed on Simba's lap.

NINETEEN
Yeah, they're haggling over the price. Simba wants ten. Moses is saying five. He's driving in the middle of the road doing about three miles an hour honking at all the pretty girls enjoying the sunshine.

SIXTY
Is that what you're smoking? I'm no expert but that looks like compressed indica to me.

NINE
Thought you said you couldn't smell your farts in this room?

SIXTY
I can see it in your eyes. It must be some good stuff because your eyes are popping out of their sockets.

NINETEEN
That's what Simba's saying.
This is some good weed, my brother. The same weed Bob Marley smoked when he was over. Exactly the same.
Moses is not buying it. Not at that price.
Not for ten. Not for anywhere near ten.
Then *WHOO-WHOO.*

SIXTY
That's the sound of the police.

NINETEEN
Yeah. Blue lights flashing. *WHOO-WHOO-WHOO*

TWENTY
That's the sound of the police.

SIXTY
If a big deal is going down you don't want to be sitting in a Beetle with a Rolls Royce front, Moses off his head haggling and unable to control his libido while driving in the middle of the road at a snail's speed. *WHOO-WHOO.*

TWENTY
That's the sound of the police.

EIGHT
You're off your fucking head
Ee-aye-addi-o
You're off your fucking head

SIXTY
You should have got out when you had the chance.

TWENTY
That's the sound of the police.

SIXTY
Now it's too late.

NINETEEN
No it's not. Moses puts his foot down, makes a run for it. A dash for freedom. Screaming engine, screeching tyres, cutting left and cutting right, corner to corner to corner. The cops right behind. First street, second, third street. *Chuck it. Out the window. Quick. Next corner.*
WHAT, THE WEED?
Yes, the weed. Chuck it out the window as I take the next corner. YOU CRAZY? YOU OUT OF YOUR MIND? DO YOU KNOW HOW MUCH...?
It's not worth going jail for. Throw it out. Frigging throw it out.
Simba finally, reluctantly, chucks the crocus bag out the window as Moses skillfully takes another corner. It slides under a parked car and Moses takes one more corner for good luck before pulling over. The cops jump out of the squad car with guns drawn like they're in Hollywood. Sirens deafening. Blue lights flashing.
HANDS UP. PUT YOUR FUCKING HANDS UP.
We climb out of the Beetle slowly, one by one, hands in the air. Two more chasing cop cars pull up – one in front and one behind. The cops are screaming.
WHY DIDN'T YOU STOP? WHY WERE YOU TRYING TO GET AWAY?
My previous traffic violations. I haven't paid the fines. You were bound to confiscate my licence plates and licence. I panicked.
The cops don't look like they believe a word of it but they're letting us go cos even though Moses' vehicle is reeking of weed they can't find nothing. It took forty minutes of negotiation but they finally let us go.

TWENTY-EIGHT
Just like that? You didn't even get charged for the smell of all that weed?

NINETEEN
We roll off into the sunset laughing our heads off and

singing *Police and thieves in the street*. Simba's still screwing.
WE'VE GOT TO GO BACK FOR THE WEED, MAN.
Moses says Simba must be crazy.
Supposing those cops saw you throw it out the car?
NOBODY SAW ME, MAN.
But supposing. Supposing somebody found it and called the cops saying I've just found a big bag of weed and then the cops put two and two together and are just waiting for us to return?
Simba wasn't in the mood for no Moses supposes.
WHO'S GOING TO CALL THE COPS IF THEY FIND A BAG OF WEED? ARE YOU CRAZY?
We're round at Moses' flat on Vanadisvägen. Moses is smoking and smoking and smoking and repeating over and over again that there's no way he is going back for the stash.
No way. Noooo... way. No way José. No way.
Simba is crying his eyes out. All he can think about is his weed and his money. Moses smokes so much weed that he eventually convinces himself to go back for the stash. It's good stuff he's smoking. It's Simba's stuff. Licked his head off. Now he knows how good the sample is, he can't resist the rest of it. So it's *see ya later* from me. I ain't a dummy, I ain't going back. I'm not going jail for Simba's weed. However good it is.

SIXTY
At last, you're starting to make sense.

NINETEEN
Catch you later.
Moses was gone. With weed on his mind. Sure 'nuff the cops are waiting. The same cops. Like they couldn't live with themselves until these jokers were behind bars.
WHAT DO YOU MEAN THIS WEED IS NOT YOURS?
Moses is a school teacher by the way. Or at least he is until he has to explain to the headmaster why he wasn't even able to phone in sick. But I definitely did not grass him up.

TWENTY-ONE
To this day Moses reckons you did.

NINETEEN
That don't make no sense, star. Why would I?

FIFTY
Moses is in a care home now by the way.

NINETEEN
Already? He's only a few years older than me.

FIFTY
Yeah. Don't know if you remember he was a diabetic. Well, he forgot to take his insulin went into a coma and lay there for days before they found him. By then his brain was gone. He can't walk. He can't talk. Can't smoke. Can't fuck.

NINETEEN
Can't fuck?! That will really piss him off. He was always pulling out his dick.

TWENTY-THREE
Remember that time in Sundbyberg when a car full of raggare pull up and you pull out your flick knife?

NINETEEN
Sunny day. One moment I'm walking, minding my own business and then the next moment a car full of raggare pull up shouting. I hadn't learned to speak the language too tough but it sounded racist. And they were driving a '58 Chevy convertible with a huge confederate flag and I just went into full Rebel Without A Cause mode. Styling it out. Pulled out a flick knife. I was totally Jimmy Dean in that scene in the planetarium. Like this was the Griffith Observatory. The raggare didn't shit themselves like they were supposed to though. They just popped open their boot and pulled out a couple of baseball bats and came after me. I didn't even have time to tell them I wasn't looking for trouble and that I was only joking. I turned and ran for my life and they came after me. My heart was jumping in my mouth as we raced through the busy shopping high street knocking over anything or anybody in our way with

full force as they gave chase past the butchers, the bakers, the bank, the bookshop. Trying to find a way. Somewhere in the distance I hear the sound of sirens. I have to find a way. Keep going. Have to get away. Close behind me I hear the shouts of abuse from the chasing pack swinging their bats. Don't stop. If they catch me I'm dead. Must get away. The sirens getting closer and louder. And then I do a mad one. Right across this dual carriageway, no looking left, right and left again.

JOOKS
Nooooooooooooooooo!

TWENTY-THREE
Other way round you mean. You're overseas.

NINETEEN
Still can't figure out how I never got killed.

JOOKS
Thank god you're alive. You made it. You survived.

NINETEEN
Matter of fact the raggare couldn't figure out how I never got run over neither. They saw the pile-up in my wake. A three-car crash following my mad dash as drivers tried to avoid running me down.

JOOKS
Oh shit. Oh no. Please tell me no one died.

NINETEEN
I don't know, you know. All I was thinking was I was safe from the raggare. I stuck two fingers up at them from the safety of the other side of the road and gave them the middle finger on top of that. And then I just ran and ran. Shitting myself.

FORTY
Flick knives. What are you like?

THIRTY-THREE
When you start trouble you've got to be prepared to finish it.

JOOKS
But what about the pile-up? You caused it. Swedish cops being Swedish cops will eventually put two and two together and you'll be banged up.

NINETEEN
No I won't. You'll never believe what happened. Turns out I didn't cause the pile-up. It wasn't me the cars were trying to avoid but7 a head-on collision. Turns out that as I run across this busy road some bloke decides to jump the verge and drive into the oncoming traffic at speed.

JOOKS
You're right, I'm never going to believe it. What a coincidence.

NINETEEN
You know what Swedes are like. Highest suicide rate in the world. The things they'll do to avoid getting out of this world alive. They're very creative when it comes to dying.

TWENTY-FIVE
Remember Böna and them?

FORTY-FIVE
RIP. OG. One of the originals. Rude Kids. *Raggare is a bunch of motherfuckers*. Big tune that. He skidded his motor across the other side of an icy road as well didn't he? At speed.

TWENTY-FOUR
You sure it was suicide?

NINETEEN
The only thing I know for sure is that raggare really are a bunch of motherfuckers. And they're all over Sweden. Remember when the Pistols played at Glädjehuset and the raggare waited outside to beat us all up? Peppe got his head kicked in. And they're racist.

TWENTY-FOUR
Oh yeah. Poor Peppe. You know how he killed himself?

TWENTY-ONE
Peppe? Noooooo. Killed himself? No way. Not Peppe.

TWENTY-TWENTY
Peppe. Dead?

TWENTY-FOUR
Jumped off the ferry between Finland and Sweden.

TWENTY-TWENTY
No way.

TWENTY-FOUR
Middle of winter when the Baltic is frozen. Ice the whole way from Stockholm to Helsinki.

TWENTY-THREE
He's dead.

TWENTY-FOUR
Yeah, old Peppe. Old weedy, stammering Peppe. Turns out he had the balls to be the baddest, bravest, maddest one of us all. Didn't you promise to link up with him? The last time you saw him. You never did, though, did you?

TWENTY-THREE
I meant to. But you know how things get. Poor Peppe. First time I saw him was down by Sergel's Torg. Kripp was riding him like a horse.

TWENTY-ONE
Yeah. Kripp's a psycho. He tried to bite my balls off one time. Next time I'll fucking kill him. Plop-Plops says Kripp's too dumb to be racist, but I swear...

JOOKS
Who's Plop-Plops?

TWENTY-THREE
Last time I saw him was at Kungsträdgården. Hardly recognized him. He was all preppy - specs, cuddly jumper and all. Not the same Peppe who was punk through and through. Looked like he had fought all his demons and won. R-E-S-P-E-C-T-able And I really did mean to see him, but I moved back to London.

JOOKS
Plop-Plops?

TWENTY-THREE
No, Peppe.

SIXTY
A lot of people have died in the making of this story and it ain't even got going yet. We still haven't figured out who is going to murder you and why. Do you honestly think you're gonna find what you're looking for?

JOOKS
You just said Plop-Plops said don't worry about it, that Kripp's too dumb even to be racist. Who is Plop-Plops?

TWENTY-TWENTY
That fucking Kripp. What a racist cunt.

NINETEEN
Kripp the cripple?

TWENTY-TWENTY
Yeah.

JOOKS
Jeez.

TWENTY-TWENTY
Smackhead. Got everyone on smack. Giving it away like sweeties at first. Nobody thought to ask. Cos he was punk through and through. Handed out the smack for free and

then when everybody was hooked he started charging.

FIFTY-EIGHT
He's a crackhead now. I hear he's working for the Swedish secret police. From crackhead to copper. You couldn't make it up. The secret policeman who doped the nation.

TWENTY-TWENTY
They are all on it.

THIRTY-THREE
Too wasted for a white riot of their own. Tee-hee.

THIRTY-SIX
I don't know, but I reckon Kripp was Säpo back then but nobody thought to ask so he got away with it. I wouldn't put it past him. He's always been undercover in my recollection.

JOOKS
I don't want to hear about Kripp or talk about the others. I remember them all. I want to talk about Plop-Plops. Who is he and what is he to you?

TWENTY-TWO
Answer him. Tell him.

TWENTY-ONE
What, the truth.

TWENTY-TWO
Yes. The whole truth.

THIRTY-THREE
He can't handle it.

JOOKS
Try me. The truth. Who is Plop-Plops? Come on, we're getting to the truth. All I need you to do is tell me who he is and what he's got to do with us?

EFFRIES

TWENTY-TWENTY
What, you're asking us to grass?

JOOKS
Well, no, not exactly.

TWENTY-TWENTY
Have you forgotten where you're from? We don't grass.

JOOKS
Technically speaking, yes. Philosophically speaking, the grass is only green if he's caught red-handed. In other words, the sound of the forest is only sound if there's someone to hear it. A grass is a grass is a grass, but that's between me and you. No one need ever know. See those buttons at the bottom of your screen, yeah, those icons. You see the one that says 'Chat', well click on it with that little plastic mouse in your hand and send me a direct message. All I want to know is who knows Plop-Plops best. It's between me and you. No one will ever know.

TWENTY-TWENTY
I'm not doing that. I'm no supergrass. However good the grass is. I'm not grassing up my mates.

JOOKS
You don't have to, mate. Just looking at the chat now, you got the most likes anyway. You and NINETEEN. Congrats. So, tell me, who is Plop-Plops? What's he got to do with us?

TWENTY-TWENTY
A mate. That's all.

TWENTY-ONE
King of the punks, the papers called him. Yeah, little old Plop-Plops, sweet sixteen, face of an angel and all that.

JOOKS
Papers. What papers?

TWENTY-ONE
Fancied himself a Sid Vicious, Plop-Plops. Anthem for doomed youth and all that. Always wilding. Always looking a fight. Always looking to get himself into more trouble than anyone else with the cops.

JOOKS
Cops. What cops?

NINETEEN
Cute kid. Undernourished. That's the punk look. He was only fifteen when we first met. Only a kid. Original angel with a dirty face. You got to love him though. Goes halves on a burger with me cos he knows I'm so hungry. Can't believe how expensive Sweden is. It's killing me. I'm always broke. No word of a lie. When his mum gives him twenty crowns for lunch he splits it with me. Down the middle. On a cheap hamburger down at Clock just off Hamngatan. He's more than a friend, he's like a brother from another mother.

SIXTY
Funny, went by Clock the other day on my pilgrimage back to Stockholm. It's a Mickey D's now.

TWENTY-TWENTY
First time we met was over by Sergels Torg. He was wearing man-size army surplus, a black beret pulled low to one side and wraparound shades and brown leather brogues too big for his feet. He talked with a lisp. *JETHUTH WATH BLACK!* he shouted at that little old lady who pushes her organ there every day, rain or shine, singing hymns to the son of God. I guess she's dead. Otherwise she'd be in her hundreds.

SIXTY
JESUS WAS BLACK, JESUS WAS BLACK.
Plop-Plops had P-S-Y-C-H-O-P-A-T-H written all over him from that very first time. I'm telling you. Stay away from him or you'll regret it.

TWENTY-TWENTY

Plop-Plops wasn't like that. His bad mind was like an acting gig. He should get an Oscar for it in the Academy Awards of life. We're all actors. The whole world is a stage. Behind the wild child mask Plop-Plops was the sweetest bloke who would share his last hamburger with me. Told the cops that. They laughed in my face.

He wouldn't kill a man? Are you drunk? Plop-Plops ain't no fucking angel. He killed a man. Take me for the last of the wikings.

TWENTY-ONE

Yeah, it's all coming back to me now. I remember. Stockholm punks we hang around. In Gallerian. You know, the shopping arcade down on Hamngatan, opposite NK. I remember Plop-Plops was supposed to crash at TWENTY-TWENTY's. On Frejgatan. Him and the beautiful Mona.

TWENTY-TWO

The one Da Vinci didn't paint.

TWENTY-ONE

You've seen her then?

TWENTY-TWO

Jeezus, yeah. Beautiful. A perfect creation of the purest art.

THIRTY-SEVEN

I saw her at the Louvre. In Paris. Japanese tourists all around her. Snapping. You know. I've seen big men try and lie and cry (maybe even die) for that girl. Beautiful.

TWENTY-ONE

If only she knew she wouldn't be like that forever. It was roses and sunshine and burgundy wine when Plop-Plops and her first got together. They enjoyed every moment of that magical moment. Just goes to show you never know because then they were crackheads together and then they're on smack and trying to sort themselves out together, see, trying to get as far away from Stockholm as they can. Away from the junk. You know. Don't know who

is the bigger smackhead – him or her. Off their heads. All
the time. You can't shut them up. But Plop-Plops didn't
show up, see. For weeks and weeks. Not a peep. Finally, he
calls in the middle of the night and says:

*Jooks, how you doing? I'm ready. Yeah, I know. I couldn't come
round when I said I was coming round. I was banged up. You
know. Yeah, a load of effries. But here I am. Ready. Outside...
Yeah, right now. In the phone box across the road... It's freezing
out here. Open up. What's the matter with you? Let me in.*

I was pissed off. I won't lie. Middle of the night is bad
enough but out of the blue and all. Two months later than
expected. I had completely forgotten about it. Who does he
think I am? What is he playing at? And, moreover:

Sod off. I'm on the job. My girl's with me. So get lost.

THIRTY-THREE
Now, why doesn't that surprise me? You're shafting your
best friend for some girl. And this is after shafting your
own mum for some girl. Do you never learn your lesson?
When are you going to control your libido?

TWENTY-ONE
Leave it out, mate. I'm trying to tell a story.

THIRTY-THREE
This is fuckries. You're so full of it. You're out there getting
laid. You were supposed to be out there studying. Where's
the degree? Be real. How many times did you actually go to
uni over there, eh? What have you got to show for it?

JOOKS
And what about Plop-Plops?

TWENTY-ONE
What about him? I can't remember no more.

JOOKS
Yeah right. What's going on? Why won't you talk about
Plop-Plops? Who the frigg is he? How comes you know
him but I don't? What's going on?

THIRTY-THREE
That's 'nuff of the fun and games. Life's too short. We all know what's going on. All except you.

SIXTY
Uhm, THREES, you better watch your mouth.

THIRTY-THREE
You better watch your mouth. Stop all this messing around. Give it to him straight. Tell it like it is so that he can get his precious sleep and we can all get out of here and go about our business, yeah? Time to start singing like a canary, TWENTY.

TWENTY-TWENTY
Don't know what you're talking about.

THIRTY-THREE
I said stop messing around. You got away with murder back there.

TWENTY-TWENTY
What you talking about?

THIRTY-THREE
Bollocks, Mr Innocent. You're dicking around the wrong prick. You got away with murder. You don't forget. Blank it. Erase it. You never forget it. Not a day goes by.

SIXTY
Mate, shut up.

TWENTY-TWENTY
You don't know what you're talking about.

THIRTY-THREE
No, you shut up. What you've conveniently chosen not to bring to memory is that you were working at the Universitets och Högskoleämbetet over on Drottninggatan. The Odenplan end. All winter long. In the post room.

Remember that was the winter you started writing for Schlager and then you and Thomas got the record deal with Abba. Remember? Remember you used to go home for lunch because Frejgatan was only about a ten minute walk away. Remember that lunchtime when you went home and the cops were there. Remember? And the next thing you know they take you down to Polishuset and charge you for murder. Remember?

TWENTY-TWENTY
I never got charged.

JOOKS
Thank god for that. I'll sue anyone who suggests otherwise.

TWENTY-TWENTY
It wasn't even me they were looking for. Two tall geezers. Blondes. Blue eyes. Outside my front door trying to break in when I get home on my lunch break. Looking for Plop-Plops's black leather jacket.

JOOKS
Plop-Plops. Again. He's all over the place like he's got something to do with everything?

TWENTY-TWENTY
And they go:
ARE YOU JOOKS? JOOKS KAMI-OLA-KAMI-OLU-WALA-JOKO.
And I go, *Yeah, why?*
They show me their IDs. They're murder squad.
Murder squad? Shit. I start shitting myself.
They say, *DOES THE NAME PLOP-PLOPS MEAN ANYTHING?*
And I go, *Depends.*
And they go, *YEAH? IN THAT CASE, SMART GUY, YOU'RE UNDER ARREST.*
And I'm like, *It was just a joke. Sorry, all right. Yeah, I know Plop-Plops. What about him?*
With that they push their way through my door and proceed to turn the place over.
What makes you think Plop-Plops's jacket is here? Of all the

places...

SHUT UP. WE ASK, YOU ANSWER. NOW, WHERE'S THE JACKET HE WAS WEARING?

I don't know. I hope you find it. But you won't find it here.

And they go, *Screw you.*

Shit, I just remembered, if they find my stash...

A couple of spliffs is all it is, cos of my asthma, from the Roskilde Festival in Denmark, you know. Only problem is I can't remember where I've stashed it. Weed's like that. Mashes your memory. Makes you forget where you hid your stash.

THIRTY-THREE

Again? You're getting used to this smuggling lark, aren't you?

TWENTY-TWENTY

A couple of spliffs. You call that smuggling? Anyway they didn't find it. And I go:

Guys, guys, as you can see I've got nothing to hide. I'm happy to help you officers in any way I can, but what's the sense in dragging me all the way to Polishuset? Come on, man, gimme a lunch break. I've got to get back to work. They'll fire me if I don't show up after lunch.

And they look at each other like, 'Let's just go. Leave him.' And just as they're stepping out the door, one of them stops in his tracks and bends down to pick something up. Looks like a black squash ball.. And he's like, *What's this?* I'm thinking, 'Anyone for tennis?' He puts it to his nose and takes a sniff.

THIS IS GOOD STUFF. THE REAL SHIT. IS THIS THE STUFF BOB MARLEY WAS SMOKING WHEN WE CAUGHT HIM AT GRÖNA LUND IN THE SUMMER?

What, you telling me that's weed?

EITHER THIS IS A NEPALESE TEMPLE BALL OR I'M A BANANA. I'M A HASHISH MASTER. I'VE GOT THE KNOWLEDGE.

Where did you get that? I've never seen that big a lump in my life. A smoker's wildest dream. I don't suppose you'd sell me a quarter, would you?

WHERE DID YOU GET IT, YOU MEAN. YOU KNOW, I WOULDN'T MIND GETTING MORE WHERE THAT CAME FROM.

There must be some mistake. On my life, that weed is yours.

EFFRIES

NOT MINE. IT WAS ON YOUR FLOOR.

You never picked it up in here. No way. Where am I going to be able to afford that much weed? I'm a frigging student.

NO USE LYING OR DENYING IT, YOU'RE A FRIGGING WHEELING-DEALING STUDENT.

You know you planted that.

WHAT DO YOU TAKE US FOR? DO WE LOOK LIKE THE PLANTING WEED KINDA COPS? THAT AIN'T EVEN FUNNY. CAREFUL WHAT YOU SAY, BOY, AND WHO YOU'RE ACCUSING, IT MIGHT GET YOU A SMACK IN THE CHOPS. THAT'S THE KINDA COPS WE ARE.

The rest of it is unreal. I don't know if it's a memory or it isn't. They cuff my hands behind my back and take me down to Polishuset and that's when the madness starts and they start accusing me of murder. They have me there for ages before they even talk to me. A couple days at least. I sat in that tiny cell for what seemed like an eternity of thinking and thinking until I thought my brain was going to explode. Day or night, same difference. Finally they unlock it and lead me out into this small room with just a table and a couple of chairs, see, and start a fight. They slap me. I slap them back. They couldn't believe it. They bundle me over and one of them just goes *WHACK* in my face as hard as he can, trying to knock my block off. I taste blood. He must have been wearing a big ring or something cos he leaves this scar, this hole in my forehead, see.

FIFTY-EIGHT
Yeah, always wondered about that. I've got that hole too.

THIRTY-THREE
We've all got it.

EIGHTEEN
I haven't.

SIXTEEN
Me neither.

TWENTY-TWENTY
And he keeps going on and on and on.

EFFRIES

I'M GONNA ASK YOU ONE MORE TIME... I'M GONNA ASK YOU ONE MORE TIME... I'M GONNA ASK YOU ONE MORE TIME.

I don't know nothing about no leather jacket. I ain't done nothing, I never done nothing. Please. Help. Stop. Noooo. No, I don't want to fight over a leather jacket I don't know nothing about.

THIS IS REALLY REALLY GOOD STUFF. I'M FLYING. HIGH. YOU REALLY, REALLY, MUST TELL ME WHERE YOU GET IT FROM. BUT FIRST, TELL ME, WHERE'S THE LEATHER JACKET YOU WERE WEARING ON THE NIGHT OF THE MURDER?

Murder? No way. I wasn't wearing a leather jacket on the night of the murder.

OH SO YOU DID DO THE MURDER.

No, of course not.

TWO PEOPLE SAW YOU.

I don't care how many people saw me, I wasn't there.

MAN'S DEAD, AND YOU'RE THE COCKSUCKER WOT DONE IT. ADMIT IT.

I didn't do it. I never murdered no one. I'm getting the shit kicked out of me for a murder I never done.

YOU TAKE US FOR MUGS? WE KNOW.

You don't know nothing. How can you? I never done nothing.

LEAVE OFF.

You leave off. First you plant weed and now you're trying to plant a murder on me.

LOOK AT THIS PICTURE. YOU RECOGNISE THAT BLACK LEATHER JACKET? RECOGNISE THE PERSON WEARING IT? WHAT DO YOU MEAN THAT AIN'T YOU? LOOKS LIKE YOU. WALKS LIKE YOU. MAN, THAT IS YOU.

Where the fuck you get that photo?

EVERYBODY IN THE BUILDING HEARD THE DEAD MAN SCREAM, 'NO, YOOKSY, NO.' YOOKSY. THAT'S YOU, ISN'T IT YOOKSY? PEOPLE STILL CALL YOU THAT IN THE ENDS. AFTER ALL THESE YEARS. WHY WOULD HE BE CALLING OUT YOUR NAME IF YOU WEREN'T THERE? HE WAS EITHER BEGGING YOU NOT TO KILL HIM OR NOT TO RAPE HIM.

What? No, I'm JOOKS, not YOOKSY. That's what they call me in the ends – JOOKS. JOOKSY.

YEAH, BUT WE'RE SWEDISH.

Is this some kind of yoke?

THE AXE OR THE MEAT CLEAVER.

Axe? Meat cleaver. Oh my god, you mean it, don't you? You're not yoking

AXE. MEAT CLEAVER. THEY'RE GOING TO LOCK YOU UP AND THROW AWAY THE KEY. UNLESS...

Unless what? Please tell me.

UNLESS THEY BRING BACK HANGING.

You're having a laugh.

LET ME GO THROUGH THE SCENARIO YOU SAY YOU WEREN'T AT ONE MORE TIME. STOP ME IF I GET ANY BITS WRONG. THIS WAS A ROBBERY GONE WRONG, YEAH?

That's bollocks.

WHICH PART?

All of it.

MATE, WHY YOU DIDN'T JUST TAKE THE MONEY AND RUN?

Cos I wasn't there.

LOOK AT YOU. FIRST YOU CHOP A MAN UP LIKE A P-R-I-C-K. THEN YOU TRY AND DENY IT LIKE A P-U-S-S-Y. NAH, MAN, THAT'S SOME FUCKRIES.

Day after day after day. The interrogation went on and on and on. Day and night. Day and night. Day and night. Round and round and round in circles.

WHERE IS THE JACKET? WHERE IS IT? WHERE'S THE JACKET?

This isn't happening. You're not for real. This is a bad dream, a nightmare.

THEY ALL SAY THAT, DON'T THEY? THEY ALL SAY THAT THEY HAVEN'T GOT IT IN THEM. THAT THEY COULDN'T MURDER SOMEONE. THEY ALL SAY THAT IT MUST BE SOME MISTAKE, DON'T THEY?

But it's true. I swear on my mother's life.

BUT YOUR MUM'S DEAD.

Okay, on my step-mother's life, I ain't got what it takes to commit murder.

YOU KNOW HOW WE FOUND HIM, DON'T YOU. AXE IN THE BACK OF HIS HEAD. STILL ALIVE.

That's amazing. Can I go now.

YOU WERE OUT OF IT THE WHOLE NIGHT. YOU DON'T REMEMBER A THING.

Not a thing.

SMASHED.

Yeah.

OUT OF YOUR HEAD.

That's right.

THIS AXE IN THE BACK OF THIS MAN'S SKULL THEREFORE HAS NOTHING TO DO WITH YOU.

Yes, I mean no, I mean yes, no, no, no. Please don't keep showing me that photo. It's horrible.

I'M JUST TRYING TO JOG YOUR MEMORY. TO REMIND YOU WHAT A HEAD LOOKS LIKE WITH AN AXE JAMMED IN THE BACK OF THE SKULL. IN CASE YOU'VE FORGOTTEN. OUT OF IT, YOU SAY. YOU COULDN'T HAVE BEEN THERE, DONE THAT, YOU SAY. IT COULDN'T HAVE BEEN YOU, YOU SAY.

Yeah.

YEAH?

Yeah. I was out of it. Completely out of it.

HOW DO YOU KNOW YOU WERE OUT OF IT IF YOU WERE OUT OF IT?

Because by the time I came to the sun was rising east of Eden. Last thing I remember, the night sky was black and the street lights were shimmering in the heavy snowfall.

OH YOU'RE A POET NOW. I THOUGHT YOU SAID YOU DON'T SMOKE WEED ON ACCOUNT OF YOUR ASTHMA?

What... what's that got to do with anything?

OI, SHUT YOUR BLOODY MOUTH. WE ASK, YOU ANSWER. DO YOU WANT ANOTHER NOSE BLEED?

In the end I couldn't take no more. I decided to just say anything. First thing that came to mind. Anything to make the madness stop. Told them what they wanted to hear. I didn't have a clue where Plop-Plops's jacket was but I told them anyway. Sent them off on a wild goose chase. Told them it was hidden in the krypt of a church. Any church. First church that came to mind. I would have said anything by then just to get them off my back. It worked. Eventually they let me go. They couldn't pin nothing on me.

THIRTY-THREE

They let you go? Just like that. Out the door. That don't make no sense. Why would they let you go just like that? Unless...

TWENTY-TWENTY
How would I know? It was like they used me, abused me then released me.

THIRTY-THREE
And you didn't think to ask them why they were letting you go.

TWENTY-TWENTY
What would I do that for? There was no evidence, I guess. They couldn't keep me there for ever and I wasn't hanging around to ask. The moment I see the light I start singing. *Hallelujah.* A wretch like me had been saved. *Hallelujah.* I took a left, took a right, left-right, left-right and end up walking straight ahead to nowhere on Gamla Brogatan. Guess who comes the other way? No Way José, the weed dealer. Don't know if you remember him. The mad one. Anyway at this time he was going around being the manager of Hocky's group, The Pain, who had just changed their name to Chatterbox and he was telling everybody how he was going to get them a big record deal and everything and cos I was writing for Schlager at the time he wanted me to do a big piece on them. So he comes up to me on Gamla Brogatan and says have you heard that Plop-Plops has been nicked for murder.
And, oh yeah, by the way, did you get that thing I put through your letterbox. That's some of the best Nepalese out there. I wanted to thank you for doing that little review of Chatterbox's new single. Nice. Nice.

JOOKS
And Plop-Plops, king of the punks. What about him?

TWENTY-TWENTY
It's like José says, he's been nicked. And he's been charged with murder. Can you believe it?

THIRTY-THREE
No I can't. Unless...

TWENTY-TWENTY
Apparently the cops found his black leather jacket stashed away in the churchyard where I said it was. What a coincidence. Can you believe it?

THIRTY-THREE
No I can't. Unless...

TWENTY-TWENTY
How could I have known that Plop-Plops actually stashed it there.

THIRTY-THREE
How could you have known, indeed, unless you knew... and then you grassed.

TWENTY-TWENTY
Call me a grass again and your arse will be grass. Like I say, Plop-Plops was supposed to come round, I didn't hear from him for ages. Turns out he had been behind bars all that time. Differently. Out in the sticks. But now he is behind bars at Stockholm Central charged with murder.

TWENTY-TWO
He was freezing his nuts off and you didn't let him crash. Jeez, what kind of mate are you? He was only a couple months late. You were spars, he's supposed to be able to spar you up any time. Day or night. That's what spars are for.

TWENTY-TWENTY
He was cool about it. He said:
Don't worry about it. I'll sort something out. See you in the next life.
I swear, that was the last I heard from Plop-Plops. And that's all. I don't know. I don't have a lot more to say.

JOOKS
The cops charged him with murder. Was he convicted?

EFFRIES

TWENTY-TWENTY
What are you trying to say?

JOOKS
Nothing. I'll keep my suspicions to myself.

EIGHT
Go home you bums
Where you come from
Go home you bums
Go home

Go home you bums
Go home you bums
Go home
Where you come from

DO YOU BELIEVE IN GOD? COS THERE'S NO GETTING OUT ALIVE.

If you put it like that, I'm a believer. I've changed my tune.

SO HAVE I. I USED TO BE A PRIEST. REMEMBER?

And a rabbi, a rasta, and an imam. How can you not believe?

I HAD NO CHOICE BUT TO CHOOSE. LISTENING TO YOU WHEN YOU NEVER USED TO BE A BELIEVER MADE MY MIND UP. YOU WERE RIGHT, LIFE IS WHAT YOU MAKE IT.

I used to be the first one to say the one wotdunnit takes the blame, the whole blame and nothing but the blame. But I ain't like that no more. I'm beginning to think that there is a master plan and we are but actors on a stage like Shakespeare said. It's like God sees and knows and has already sussed what I'm going to do so I may as well do it.

ONE OF MY BROTHERS IS LIKE YOU. I LOVE HIM TO BITS, BUT WE CAN'T EVEN GO TO A LAP DANCING CLUB WITHOUT HIM HAVING TO CONFESS ALL TO HIS MISSUS WHO WILL THEN PICK UP THE PHONE AND TELL MY MISSUS AND THEN, BEFORE YOU KNOW IT, ALL HELL BREAKS LOOSE AND I END UP CATCHING FIRE FOR NOTHING. LIKE THE TIME HE COULDN'T CONTROL HIS LIBIDO WITH A CERTAIN ATTRACTIVE WOMAN WHO HE WASN'T MARRIED TO. HEY, IT HAPPENS. HE WAS DRUNK AND SHE WAS DRUNK AND.... WELL, I WAS DRUNK TOO. I BEGGED HIM NOT TO MENTION IT TO HIS WIFE WHO WOULD THEN MENTION IT TO MY WIFE. I BEGGED AND I BEGGED AND I BEGGED. INFORM YOUR OTHER HALF ON A NEED-TO-KNOW BASIS. BUT MY BRO INSISTED. HE COULDN'T LIVE WITH HIMSELF OTHERWISE. WE'RE NOT EVEN CATHOLIC YET HE'S GIVING ME ALL THIS YADDA-YADDA-YADDA. IF YOU WANT TO COME CLEAN TAKE A LONG HOT SHOWER.

THIRTY-ONE
What a load of effries. I've got the feeling that it's just about to get x-rated. My question again, should the little'uns even be here listening to this?

NINE
Oi, I'm warning you, none of that 'little'uns'.

THIRTY-ONE
It's way past their bedtimes and, if we're getting candid, this is no place for kids. Everyone under TWELVE needs to leave this meeting now.

ELEVEN
Are you having a laugh? You want us to leave when everything's just about to kick off.

JOOKS
No, he's got a point. You lot are off the rails already. You don't need more effries in your life.

ELEVEN
You can shut your big gob and all. Call yourself JOOKS? You're a disgrace. You're the worst person I could ever become. An embarrassment. You shit yourself here, you shit yourself there and you can't even work out who is trying to kill you. Can't you see? It's obvious. The person trying to kill you is —

THIRTY-ONE
Hey, what happened there? You cut him off.

JOOKS
No. I mean yes. I mean, I don't know. If I did it was an accident but I don't think I did. I didn't touch anything.

THIRTY-THREE
I don't believe this. What have you done? ELEVEN was just

about to tell us whodunnit and you cut him off.

JOOKS
I didn't mean to. I didn't even touch anything, I swear. I was about to... I was reaching for my Participant Management window to remove ELEVEN and unders but before I touched anything he disappeared.

THIRTY-THREE
Just as this whole mystery was about to be revealed. That's convenient.

JOOKS
That's the god's honest truth. It must have switched off his end.

THIRTY-THREE
Get him back. What are you waiting for.

JOOKS
Let's see if he comes back up cos I have no way of getting him back. Meanwhile let me get rid of all the other youngers before they all disappear on me also. So, TEN, NINE, EIGHT, SEVEN, SIX - see ya. Wouldn't want to be ya.

TEN, NINE, EIGHT, SEVEN, SIX
Fuck y–

THIRTY-THREE
Oh my word, for f–sake. Will someone put a full stop to all this nonsense.

JOOKS
But I can't. I don't know how to.

SIXTY
What about your host privileges?

JOOKS
That's just it. The ex-priest is the host. I'm only the sub–

host so there are certain privileges I don't have. I haven't got the invites. The priest sent them out. I don't even know how he managed to get you all up in here.

THIRTY-THREE
And you say you don't trust me. I'm starting to have my doubts about you. Who are you?

JOOKS?
No, I mean it, who are you really? You are one lucky geezer to get away with murder without grassing Plop-Plops up? Where did you tell the cops the jacket was again? Which church?

TWENTY-TWENTY
First church that came to my head – Sofia Kyrka, you know in Vitabergsparken in Söder.

THIRTY-THREE
Yeah, wherever.

TWENTY-TWENTY
Totally random. I just wanted them off my back. I would have said anything.

THIRTY-THREE
And you told the cops it was in the crypt? That is a weird coincidence. That's exactly where they found it. Spooky. They didn't even have to search for it. It was exactly where you said it was.

TWENTY-TWENTY
I know. It's unbelievable.

THIRTY-THREE
Say that again. That's why I wouldn't dream of calling you a grass. JOOKS on the other hand...

EIGHT
Whispering grass

EFFRIES

Don't tell the trees...

TWENTY-EIGHT
Thought you disconnected the little'uns. What's EIGHT doing here?

JOOKS
I don't know. I'm trying to remove him from this meeting but it's not working. I can't for some reason.

TWENTY-TWENTY
Still doesn't make me a grass.

SIXTY
That's not the way Plop-Plops tells it. You say one thing, he says another.

EIGHT
Mary took her pussy
And put it in a bucket
Every time that cat got out
The dogs would try to fuck it.

JOOKS
Shut up. You're not supposed to be here any more. Nor are your crude songs.

SIXTY
And if Plop-Plop's side of the story was to ever come out, well, it's goodbye fame, it's goodbye fortune, it's goodbye 'next stop Hollywood'. And goodbye legacy.

JOOKS
Goodbye fucking Plop-Plops. I'll kill him if his point of view ever comes out. No more Mr Nice Guy. No more voice of the nation. I'll fucking murder him. So what's he saying? Is he saying I dunnit?

SIXTY
All I'm saying is that's not the way Plop-Plops tells it, is

it Two-Three?

JOOKS
Am I the only one who doesn't know the way Plop-Plops
tells it?

TWENTY-THREE
I ran into him in Vasastan. One stormy night on
Bryggerigatan. He was walking into an apartment building.
Saw each other at the same time and he was like:
*Yooks, how come you looking like you've theen a ghost? You
couldn't lend us a couple hundred crowns could you? You know,
like I used to lend you back in the day. I'm a little short.*
I was like:
*Fuck, Plop-Plops, ain't you supposed to be doing time? I didn't
know you were out.*
And he was like:
*Yes me friend, yeah, I done my time. I'm back on road again.
Cheers. One more hundred? I'll pay you back. But what happened
to you? Look at the thtate of you, Yooksy. You've been eating too
many of those Marabou chokladkakors. They've gone to your
thtomach. It's huge.*
Anyway, he tells me, he played the Swedish system and
got out in 913 days. He knew he was going to get time
no matter what, it was just a question of how long. So he
went on a mad one until they had no other choice but to
lock him up in a nut house instead of a prison so he only
served a couple of years and a bit.
*For real? Let me tell you, YOOKS, the nut house ain't no holiday
camp neither. Prison over the nut house any day. Only behind
prison bars, I'd be doing another twenty years for a crime I didn't
commit. It's pros and cons, you know. All you have to do in the
nut house is prove you're thane and they let you out. That's easy
when you're thane. Only took two and a half years to convince
them that I was not the Plop-Plop I used to be. 913 days, man. I
counted every thingle one of them thunthets. Did my time in my
own little way, causing as little trouble as pothible. They finally
believed that I was no longer a danger to thothiety and they
released me and let me go. You know what Sweden's like, right?
Those two and a half years were hell, I can't lie. But I did the time,*

even though it was you that did it. Like I thay, you saved my arth... so I thaved yours. I took the rap. But you're the murderer.

TWENTY-TWENTY
Fuck is he talking about?

TWENTY-THREE
Exactly what I said.
Fuck you talking about?
And he goes:
Don't tell me you've gone about your business and forgotten about what happened while I'm out here doing time.
I didn't know what to think cos you did such a good job of erasing most of it. Good job Plop-Plops remembers every detail. So I followed him into the apartment building and upstairs to the third floor where he introduced me to his new girlfriend, Rosie. She's apparently a member of the Swedish royal family. Can you believe it? From convicted murderer to one cock in the royals. That's Plop-Plops all over. Always landing on his feet on account of how cute he is. Especially with that lithp. On this stormy, stormy, kinda scary night the lightning flashed and the thunder rumbled and in the candle-lit backdrop of this vast cavern of an apartment (many times bigger than your standard studio everyone else lives in) Plop-Plops told his version of the story like he had been rehearsing this moment for 913 nights:
I thaved your arth back there, JOOKS.

TWENTY-TWENTY
I ain't got no idea what he's on about.

TWENTY-THREE
Like I say, these are just Plop-Plops's words:
Last time I saw you we was round Johnny Wanker's, remember, and everything is cool and we're off our heads and the music is blathting loud and the neighbours are banging on the theiling complaining and I tried to turn it down, we all did but we couldn't cos we were all so out of it that we kept turning it up even louder instead. After a while of giggling our heads off I path out and, I don't know if you remember this Yooksy, but when I wake up I

EFFRIES

see Johnny Wanker fucking you up the arth.

TWENTY-TWENTY
What? No way. Never happened. Not in a month of Mondays.

TWENTY-THREE
Plop-Plops says it did:
You thaved my arth, man, so I had to thave yours.
He says no way was he the one with the axe but he took the
blame for you. He says it was just like you said, that he was
supposed to stay at your gaff and then you said no cos you
were on the job with your girl in her flat you were living in.
He had nowhere else to stay so he was just walking the icy
streets, keeping warm smoking ciggies when he sees you
coming down the same said streets of Stockholm from the
other direction, wondering what you should do and where
you should kip for the night and he's thinking, that's how
you spell S-E-R-E-N-D-I without the P-I-T-Y.
*Therves you right, you arth. You wouldn't let me thtay at yours
and now you don't have yours to thtay in.*
Cos not for the first time, but for the last time, your girl
rolled her eyes on you and kicked you out. Called the cops
on you. So you had to leave before they got there and nicked
you for being there. Plop-Plops says he ain't the kind of
punk who holds a grudge for long so it didn't take him more
than a minute to realise that two heads are better than one
and, if it came to it, two crotches are better than one when
you're freezing your nuts off. Anyway, according to Plop-
Plops, you two were cuddling in a doorway to stay warm
through the night when along comes Johnny Wanker. You
remember Johnny, don't you? From Johnny Wanker and
the Master Baters.

NINETEEN
He's a wrong'un. Don't trust him. He may as well have
KKK tattooed across his forehead.

TWENTY-THREE
The last person in the world you expect to see in the middle
of the night on the streets of Stockholm in winter. Johnny

laughs his head off when he sees you two snogging and says to Plop-Plops:

Listen, come over and stay by me for the night. I'll keep you warm. Crash on my sofa.

He looks right through you like you don't exist until Plop-Plops points out you need somewhere to crash and all cos you couldn't survive out here without someone to cuddle. Johnny Wanker acts like he's only just seen you and says, cool, you can both crash at his place round the corner. And you both go round there, to his tiny little etta down by Östermalmstorg and everything is cool and the music is loud and you're all off your heads on some serious weed and the neighbour's banging on the ceiling but you're all too stoned to do anything about it. After a while, Plop-Plops passes out. He reckons Johnny must have sprinkled some acid in the spliff, so he's completely out of it, and when he eventually wakes up he thinks he must still be tripping cos he sees you all lit up like a christmas tree and being fucked up the arse by Johnny Wanker.

TWENTY-TWENTY
What the f-

NINETEEN
Didn't I say the devil is a dangerous guy.

TWENTY-THREE
Yes, fucking you up the arse. Hear me out, see if the cap fits. I knew you were going to deny it but, remember, you're out of it, you're tripping too, and even if you did remember any of it you've blocked it out of your memory and, therefore, our memories. So we can't help you. That's what Freud reckons. The only living witness - apart from you - to what happened is Plop-Plops. He's done his time. Why should he lie? He says when he saw Johnny Wanker fucking you up the arse he was surprised at first cos he didn't think you were his type. He always thought Johnny was an undercover racist not an undercover rapist. But then he saw the tears rolling down your cheeks.

I couldn't thtand there and not do nothing. You were biting tho hard on the pillow thtuffed down your throat, your eyes were bulging.

And Plop-Plops starts shitting himself cos he knows who's next. Johnny Wanker was already licking his chops at the prospect. Fucking eyes closed, salivating, he didn't see the elbow come flying in his face. Smack on the bridge of his nose. With a rapid flow of blood down each nostril, he shrugs his head clear and takes a moment to compose himself but he doesn't stop fucking you. Plop-Plops jumps on top of him, kicking and punching and trying to strangle him but he doesn't stop fucking you. By the time Plop-Plops finally manages to pull him off your arse Johnny Wanker has satisfied himself.

You should have theen your watery eyes, red as hell, giving me the scariest look I have ever theen. I knew, the moment I thaw the hellfire in your eyes, that Johnny Wanker was a dead man. Johnny Wanker didn't thee that look. He discards you like a bitch and turns his attention to me.

You pull yourself off the bed, somewhat gingerly, and when you see the blood on your hand from your arse you go absolutely ballistic, smashing Johnny with everything and anything you could grab. This huge glass ashtray by the sofabed came crashing down on his head. Then you split his eye open with that old flick knife of yours that was in your coat pocket hanging behind the front door. Blood everywhere. Johnny howls like a lone wolf, his carnal mind arrested momentarily. You are still going berserk, like a man possessed, smashing him and smashing him in the face with the frying pan from the kitchen but none of it seems to work. Johnny with his one and a half eyes is a hard man fe dead. All he wants to do is fuck Plop-Plops and no matter what you whack him with he just keeps coming. With blood streaming down his face he catches Plop-Plops in a headlock and starts pulling down his trousers. Then you go in the kitchenette and return with an axe and a meat cleaver. Plop-Plops screams *NO, YOOKSY NO!* What happened next is so gruesome Plop-Plops refused to go into the details. Suffice to say when an axe is embedded in the back of the skull it's like a sword in a stone.

I'll leave the rest to your imagination, Plop-Plops said.

That should have been it. Over and done. But it wasn't. Johnny Wanker recoiled like a snake from the axe blow but, shit, he was still alive - still breathing, still writhing, still slithering and wriggling. Still trying to fuck Plop-Plops's arse.

TWENTY-TWENTY
You're talking like you believe Plop-Plops. The cap don't fit. That's not how it happened. I wasn't getting fucked up the arse by nobody. I think I would remember that.

FIFTY-NINE
I believe you.

TWENTY-TWENTY
Thank you. Means a lot. It's the truth. I don't think any of you know what it's been like, what I've been going through all this time. How I torture myself over this.

TWENTY-FIVE
Believe. That fucking up the arse is unbelievable.

THIRTY-THREE
What about me?

TWENTY-TWENTY
What about you?

THIRTY-THREE
I don't believe you.

TWENTY-TWENTY
I don't believe this. Who gives a fuck what you believe?

TWENTY-THREE
Plop-Plops says you did it. We're going to have to take his word for it. He says you did it to save his arse so he had to save your arse for saving his arse when he tried to save your arse, so he told ol' bill it had nothing to do with you and that it was all him. He was going down no matter

what cos they found Johnny Wanker's blood on him, and he didn't see no sense in you both going down if you got away with it. He knew how to play the system and he played it in your favour.

TWENTY-TWENTY
You don't seriously believe that that's what happened?

THIRTY-THREE
No, I said I don't believe you. I didn't say I don't believe Plop-Plops.

TWENTY-TWENTY
Come to think of it, it was Plop-Plops who was getting fucked up the arse. Yeah, Plop-Plops. That's right. Now I remember. It's all coming back to me. Plop-Plops was being fucked up the arse. The weed tripped me out, I won't lie. I must have passed out. I woke up to moans and groans and when I got up I saw Johnny Wanker doing Plop-Plops doggystyle. I was about to jump Johnny and pull him off when I saw this look on Plop-Plops's face and, I swear, if I'm not mistaken, he winked at me as if to say do you want a go and all. And I just thought, fuck, get me out of here. And I was just about to close the front door behind me when I hear Plop-Plops scream, *NO, YOOKSY, NO!* So I rush back in and, you won't believe what Johnny Wanker was doing to Plop Plops...

JOOKS
Yeah... go on... what was he doing?

TWENTY-TWENTY
Nah man, I can't say... nah, leave it, let me keep it to myself. But you can understand why Plop-Plops completely lost it and went berserk can't you?

JOOKS
What the fuck was he doing?

TWENTY-TWENTY
I said I'm not saying. If you saw what I saw, trust me,

you would never forget it. It stays with you forever. Every minute of the day. The image never goes away. I wouldn't wish that on you. None of you.

THIRTY-THREE
We've got to ask. It's central to your story. It ain't a minor detail. What the fuck was Johnny Wanker doing to Plop-Plops?

TWENTY-TWENTY
Well, put it this way, have you ever seen two blokes fucking each other up the arse at the same time?

THIRTY-EIGHT
NOOOOOOOOOOOOOOOOOOOOOO...!!

FORTY-NINE
Oh fuck, oh fuck. Why d'you have to tell us that?

TWENTY-TWENTY
You told me to.

THIRTY-THREE
But not the fucking details.

TWENTY-TWENTY
I can't unsee what I saw.

FORTY-NINE
Neither can we. We can't unhear what we've just heard. I'm not sure if any of us will ever be able to remove the image from the forefront of our minds, thank you very much.

TWENTY-TWENTY
Okay, I'll shut up then, I won't say any more.

FORTY-NINE
You might as well.

EFFRIES

NINETEEN
You've already messed us all up.

FORTY NINE
Yeah, you can't stop now. In for a penny in for a pound.
So to speak. Shit, you're right about the image not going
away though.

TWENTY-TWENTY
Okay. So without going into how I managed to get Johnny
Wanker to stop doing what he was doing to Plop-Plops,
let's just say I managed to get him to stop doing what he
was doing to Plop-Plops. It wasn't easy. Cos at the same
time I had to get Plop-Plops to stop doing what he was
doing to Johnny Wanker.

THIRTY-THREE
Here we go again. You can't just leave it at that. You've
got to tell us how. You can't just say I got him to stop but
don't ask me how. We need to know. It's also central to
the story. Surely.

FORTY-NINE
No. For goodness sake, no. I don't want to know. We don't
need to know. Let's just take his word for it.

TWENTY-TWENTY
And you know the look you said Plop-Plops said I had when
I was being otherwise engaged from behind, according to
him, well that's the exact same look that Plop-Plops had
on his face when I managed to get Johnny Wanker to stop
doing what he was doing. I've only ever seen eyes like that
on the devil in the movies. You know, red hot. Blazing.
After I manage to get Johnny Wanker to stop doing what
he's doing, Plop-Plops tells me to get lost. That he was
going to deal with the rest himself.
Thtart running, he says.
I didn't need to be told twice. I took off out of it. Next
thing I know the cops are trying to break into my flat on
Frejgatan. That's what happened. That's why Plop-Plops

keeps saying I saved his arse so he saved my arse. He took the blame for it. The whole thing. Like I wasn't even there. That's why the cops let me go, I guess, not cos I grassed him up. And I definitely, definitely, did not get fucked up the arse.

SIXTY

That's not what Plop-Plops told me. I bumped into him too the other day on my pilgrimage back to Stockholm, by that youth club down in Rågsved where Ebba Grön used to play. What was it called? Fyran? He was giving it the old 'king of the punks', milking it. Remember Plop-Plops got nothing but props from the punks when he came out from doing time. Treated like a hero. Nobody liked Johnny Wanker so they acted like his murder was just one big misunderstanding. By now Plop-Plops is a legend. A proper smackhead, though, flaking away with the years. He can't control his bowels at all. Stinks to high heaven. Spends all day trying to avoid people he owes money to. I barely recognised him but he recognised me straight away and must have remembered that he owed me that cash you lent him all those years ago, Two-Three, cos he tried to duck out. Still walks like a crab. As soon as I saw the walk, I knew, and I called out.
Plop-Plops, it's me, Jooks. It's been time. Stuff the money you owe me. I'm not after you for that.
He said he couldn't remember when he last ate so I buy him a burger for old time's sake but they refused to let us sit and eat in because he was stinking so much. We were chasing away the customers so the manager chased us out. We find some nice park to sit and chew the fat instead. Plop-Plops nyamed the burger like a beast that hadn't eaten since the long cold winter. And we eventually cae round to talking about the murder. At first he didn't want to, said I still owed him, so I gave him a couple of hundred crowns and then I couldn't stop him talking.

TWENTY-THREE

Oh no, you can't give him more money. That money will be in the hands of the Colombians before you can say, ABBA backwards. I bet the moment your cash touched his palm he was off like a shot to the pusherman.

SIXTY
He was but he managed to score just round the corner and came back. By now he was flying, I ain't lying. He had a motor on his mouth.

You thtill owe me, Yooks. Your girl kicked you out and my girl kicked me out and we're both on the late night thtreets wondering what to do when we bump into Johnny Wanker and we go up to his plathe and thmoke thome pipes. You're off your head. You trip out and thtart getting para, accusing Johnny of mixing some heavy thtuff with the weed.

TWENTY-ONE
I don't remember being there. Don't remember not being there either. It's a moment in mist.

TWENTY-TWENTY
Me neither.

SIXTY
Plop-Plops was there. And he says you were there. He says, yes, now he remembers, he woke up in the middle of the night with something big and strong trying to split his backside. Johnny Wanker was attempting to fuck him up the arse, but luckily you came in from behind and whacked him with all your might in the back of the head with the heavy ashtray. He says Johnny Wanker recoiled and turned his head at an odd angle and just stared you in the eyes with a look that either said 'How could you?' or 'How dare you?' Plop-Plops couldn't read it too tough. And then you whacked him again, as hard as you could, with all your might, this time right on the temple. Johnny Wanker's scream *NO, YOOKSY, NO!* was caught and suspended in mid-echo as he looked up at you, pleading, cursing, hissing, spitting and gurgling. You hit him over and over and over and over again. But he still didn't die. And then you rushed into the kitchen, hands all icky with blood, and found an axe.

JOOKS
Jeez, man. I don't want to hear this any more. I don't want to hear any more. I know I'll regret it if I do. For the rest of my life.

SIXTY
Yeah I get that but wait. It gets worse. Really bad. Plop-Plops says that you were like a man possessed. As if the spliff, and the coke that Johnny Wanker had sprinkled in it, had sent you off your head or something. And you go to the kitchen and come back with this axe.

JOOKS
Noooooooooo....

TWENTY-TWENTY
This is all bollocks. I swear none of this is true.

SIXTY
I know, I know... but these are the brutal facts. This is what Plop-Plops says happened. His version. Yeah, his revised version. He says, naked from the waist down he grabs the axe off you and stares you down and says he'll take care of it:
Whatever happens just keep your mouth shut. This is my axe to grind. You get me? As far as you are concerned you are not here, this never happened.
So then he got arrested and when they found his black leather jacket he got charged. He couldn't believe it because that was the main bit of evidence against him and that's when he knew you had grassed him up. Because you're the only one who knew where that jacket was. Because you're the one who put it there. Because you took the wrong jacket. Remember all you punks wore black leather jackets. In your hurry to escape the scene you picked up his black leather jacket, he knows that because he leaves the scene shortly after but he can't find his jacket, he can only find yours and so he takes that with him to save your arse and goes and chucks it in the sea down by Slussen, you know, by where the St Petersburg ferry goes. So you

can imagine his surprise when the cops present him with his leather jacket which they say he had hidden in some church. He still can't understand why you grassed him up. After all he was doing for you by taking the blame for everything. Nevertheless, when he saw how racist the cops were (all they were trying to do was pin the whole thing on you) he told them you weren't even there. Then they tried to get him to say that you had put him up to it. They just wanted him to say, yeah, it was the 'neger', because it was unbelievable that a cute lite blonde-haired Swedish kid like him would do such a gruesome thing. It was more believable that this big black guy from somewhere in Africa had put him up to it. But Plop-Plops wasn't having it. Not a word of it. He knew their racist game. So he left you right out of it. Insisted that you had nothing to do with it and you didn't even know nothing about nothing and you were just some random black who couldn't even help them with their enquiries because you weren't even there and that if they wanted some other random black guy to pin it on why not try Sidney, you know that Nigerian guy who runs that disco Big Brother over in Östermalm. You know, the bloke who beat you up that time in Skivfabriken.

FIFTY
I read somewhere that he died not too long ago. To be fair he is a legend. The African man who introduced disco to Sweden. How come you two got into that ruck in the record shop back then? I've always wanted to know.

TWENTY-TWENTY
Long story. Bollocks. Who is going to believe this nonsense?

SIXTY
Plop-Plops goes:
The cops never liked me, thee. They was always out to get me. Too blond, too strong, you know. Remember my girl, my ex Mona? Pretty, dark-hair, beautiful girl. Da Vinci should have painted her. Because everybody in Stockholm was on smack, she and I decided to move out to her hometown, Karlstad, to get as far away as we could from all the other smackheads. I loved that

girl, you know, YOOKSY. I wasn't with her for the thex, which was amazing but I just loved her. You know what I mean by love, YOOKS? Can't live without her, can't live within her. She begs me not to go back to Stockholm, to stay another night, another day. But I needed to collect the records that I left round yours. And we got into an argument about should I or shouldn't I, and you know what Mona's like with that enigmatic thmile of hers – volatile. One moment she's the most beautiful woman in the world and the next she's got this really ugly thide to her. Anyway, we get into a fight and she punches me in the eye and my eyeball falls out of its socket and when she sees that she starts thcreaming and thcreaming and, realising she was in big trouble, calls the cops and tells them to come and get me cos I attacked her first and to protect herself she had to scratch my eyeballs out. So the cops come. Arrest me. Put my eyeball back in its socket and take me down the nick. When Mona sees that she hasn't blinded me for life she starts repenting and telling the cops that it was all one big mistake and, ordinarily, they would have let me out but, would you believe it, a law was passed that very day in the Thwedish parliament, to protect women who accuse their partners of domestic violence then recant the day after in the cold light of day when they start weighing up everything they stand to lose. The law now states that the police have got to stick to the original complaint and put the man in jail. It changed that very day. Can you believe it? Anyway that's the reason I didn't reach your yard on the night I thaid I would, I was in the hole in Karlstad nick. And when I show up round yours your girl, you know, the ugly one, gives me a screw face and says she doesn't want me around. You saw it. Was it cos we got wasted on that thpliff? I mean what's the matter with her? I'm your thpar. I don't mind if I have to sleep in the shower. Or was it cos I kicked in the door when I thought you were only joking when you told me to 'thod off' when I called you from the phonebox across the road? How was I to know you were in the middle of a shag? I was thinking, you lot need to do something about that lock, y'know. It wasn't even really a kick, more like a flick of my leg.

TWENTY-ONE
I remember this now. How could anyone forget that screw face from your girl?

TWENTY-TWO
And to make it worse, she wraps you round her little finger like you're two inches tall and belittes you:
'Do you pay the rent? Do you pay the gas? Do you pay the electricity? No, you bloody well don't. I'm fed up of you inviting your hoodlum friends to stay the night in my tiny studio flat? An etta. No room to thwing a cat. How do you expect me to maintain my modesty with a complete thtranger in the room? You have zero consideration for my feelings, tho I think you'd better go.'

TWENTY-TWENTY
She lay down the law and started chucking all my stuff out of her flat. I was homeless. It was minus 10 out there, snow everywhere. It was the middle of the night and I am out on the streets. Yeah, it's all coming back to me now. It was Plop-Plops who left me for dead. Not the other way round. It was freezing. The amount of people I tried to call from one of them phone boxes at Stureplan. Nobody answered. D'you remember? Everybody was asleep. Nobody answered except old Uffe and he told me to piss off cos of that time when I got off with his bird by accident and I didn't even know he knew about it. What a time to find out that he knew about it all along. D'you remember? So there I was walking the streets thinking, tonight will be the night when I die. Then I bump into Plop-Plops and we start hugging up just to stay warm - no homo. So by the time Johnny Wanker comes out of nowhere and offers somewhere to kip for the night we nearly bit his frozen hands off.
I've only got room for one, he goes. *It's such a tiny flat. Ip dip dog shit, who's it. Sorry Yooks, you lose.*
And he takes Plop-Plops by the hand and they head off.
Sorry Yooks, Plop-Plop says as they disappear into the snowdrift. *There's no point in both of uth freezing our bollocks off and you were going to leave me out here to freeze when your mithus kicked me out so I guess you now know how to spell S-E-R-E-N-D-I without the P-I-T-Y.*
And that was that. They went off, hand in hand, and I never saw them again that night. I wasn't there when the murder happened. It's just Plop-Plops made me think I was and put the thought in my mind because he came round

later the next morning and he was off his head on speed and got me hallucinating on some of them mushrooms he brought round and he started talking about how WE murdered Johnny Wanker and how HE deserved it and how WE picked up an axe and how WE had hidden his leather jacket in a church to be disposed off at a later date. But I didn't know which church and I couldn't have imagined it would be in the crypt when I thought I was sending ol' bill on a wild goose chase in search of it. And before I knew it, Plop-Plops had me believing that I was there (remember, I was hallucinating) and that Johnny Wanker said I've got room for both of you and that WE both followed him down the road to his place in Östermalmstorg and we smoked a few spliffs to warm us up and two-twos WE were out of it: *Next thing I know I've woken up in the middle of the night to a muffled cry. Our good thamaritan fucking you up the arth, you biting hard on his pillow. Well, you don't forget thomething like that in a hurry, do you? I must have thnapped cos the next thing I know I went abtholutely beserk. I jumped on top of him, tried to pull him off you but I hadn't protected my bollocks and, thtill fucking you from behind, he manages to reach behind him and thqueeze my nuts as hard as he could. I fucking thcreamed with pain. Remember? My theed thtarted to bleed. I thought it was you doing the thqueezing, Yooks, I didn't think Johnny Wanker's hand could reach that far back. That's why I thcreamed 'NO YOOKSY NO!' And Johnny Wanker turns round to me with this weird look on his face and says, 'You're next.' I managed to prise his hand off my balls and get away. I should have just run out the door but I couldn't leave you. I ran into the kitchen in panic. That's where I thaw the meat cleaver and the axe. No way was I going to let him fuck me when he was done with you.*

What a load of effries. Like I say, I was hallucinating.

FORTY-FOUR

That's not the way the cops see it. According to their investigation there was Plop-Plops, Johnny Wanker and a mysterious third person involved in the orgy. A black guy who they thought would be very easy to spot in a blonde and blue-eyed beauty spot like Sweden but who to this day has remained elusive. The police report relies heavily on the testimony of the neighbours who heard everything. Plop-Plops and the unidentified black guy were having sex so loudly it woke Johnny Wanker up and when he tried to interrupt and pull Plop-Plops off you, that's when Plop-Plops flipped, went wild and found the axe and did Johnny Wanker in. Initially they thought you were taking Plop-Plops from behind. They just assumed that the big black guy must have been bossing the little white guy. No way the other way round. They were working off the premise that whoever was on top was the one who murdered Johnny Wanker. But when they realised it was all about Plop-Plops they realised they had to find the semen stains. That's where the black leather jacket comes in.

TWENTY-TWENTY
Nonsense. What do you know about the way the cops see it?

FORTY-FOUR
I saw the records. Live and direct. A vague memory of this has bothered me for yonks. Just like you, I haven't been able to sleep at night. So I know what you're talking about. You've done a good job blanking it, I'll give you that, but a gangbang is a gangbang. If you've been to one you never completely forget it. I was kept awake all night and every night for what seemed like forever by a residual recollection, the faintest of a vague memory. But it's so... REAL. Couldn't sleep a wink. Every time I dozed off it felt like a huge dildo was being shoved in my orifice. It's an uncomfortable feeling I can assure you. If you think about it, if you really think about it. I mean, you can't tell that to your missus lying in the bed beside you. You're knackered, completely whacked, unable to sleep, for yonks, no exaggeration, and the moment you start dozing off you get a big hard prick where you least expect it, well, you wouldn't be able to sleep a wink either, I can assure you. I don't care who you are.

JOOKS
Mate, we get it. No need to elaborate. Can we get on with the story? How come you know what was in the police report?

FORTY-FOUR

Tookie told me. Thank god for him. That day his girl got in touch with me after seeing a doc I did for Channel 4, was the day that changed my life. She gets in touch and says: *You may be related to my boyfriend. I think he's your brother.*

I was like, yeah, sure, course he's my kid brother. I haven't seen him since he was like two. Anyway, as most of you know, it turns out that he lives in Copenhagen, turns out he's a murder squad copper out there. So the first thing he does when we get in touch and he finds out I had been living in Sweden, is get some Swedish coppers to check me out on their database, as you do if you're ol' bill and, lo and behold, your name pops up and there's a whole file on you because they initially believed you were linked to the murder of Johnny Wanker. Turns out you were just some random black man with a big dick that they picked up. Plop-Plops confessed to everything. He was fucking some random black guy (the elusive 'third man') and Johnny Wanker was fucking him Plop-Plops and the black guy was fucking Johnny Wanker. In a circle. At the same time.

EIGHT

Ring-a-ring o' roses...

TWENTY-TWENTY

At least that proves it wasn't me. I'm not that flexible.

FORTY-FOUR

The police report says as unbelievable as it sounds, on closer examination it proved to be credible. It happened. They don't know how it was done but it was done. They reckon them lot were so high they believed they could fly and that anything was possible. We all know what it's like to be out of it. And according to the police report them lot were smoking the same weed Bob Marley smoked when he played in Stockholm in the summer of 1980 at Gröna Lund. So as far as the police report is concerned you had absolutely nothing to do with the case and, unless some future criminal technology is able to prove otherwise by tying you to the place and moment of the murder, you are to be regarded as completely innocent. Plop-Plops told them it was an open and shut case because he was confessing to everything. And that it was him who shouted 'NO, YOOKSY, NO!' to try to frame you initially because he knew that the police would sooner believe that it was a black man who killed Johnny Wanker than an angelic-looking white boy, but now that he had found God he had seen the error of his ways and was confessing to absolutely everything.

THIRTY-THREE
God? Don't give that crackhead any more crack is all I'll say.

TWENTY-TWENTY
So I hope that proves that I am innocent once and for all. You lot didn't believe me. Do you honestly think that in these days when Sweden is such a racist country, do you honestly think that they would have let me go if they had any evidence that I was involved? Come on, man. You KNOW the score. Why would they have put the pretty little white boy behind bars and let me go? Or did you not think of that?

THIRTY-THREE
Fair point, I won't lie.

JOOKS
Damn. This is the most gross story. I cannot comprehend.

TWENTY-TWENTY
So don't you lot owe me an apology or something?

FORTY-FOUR
No, Plop-Plops owes you an apology. He tried to frame you first by sending ol' bill round to yours when they were looking for his black leather jacket, which was how ol' bill brought you into the frame of the investigation to start with. He's the one who was grassing you up until God found him.

LAST LOAD

LYDIA
JK. Welcome back from the dead. You're waking up just in time. The trolley dolly's coming down the aisle with some lunch. Boy, that was a deep sleep, though. Five hours straight. Right through the bumpiest turbulence I've ever experienced. Passengers were screaming but you were like waking the snoring dead. I've never heard anything so loud. Like a foghorn. Honestly. And in between, the stories you were telling. Like Goldilocks and the three bears. Do you always talk in your sleep?

JOOKS
Uurrgh! I needed that. A good stretch after a good sleep. I'm so knackered. What was I saying in my sleep?

LYDIA
All sorts. I couldn't keep up. Halley's comet.

JOOKS
Haley. Bill Haley and his Comets.

LYDIA
Yeah. And a shoe bomber.

JOOKS
THE shoe bomber. There's only one.

LYDIA
And you're firing blanks.

JOOKS
That's a long story. You see, I sent these bullets off for PR.

LYDIA
And all the people you've murdered.

JOOKS
Oh fuck.

LYDIA
There was this one bloke that you murdered and the axe got stuck in the back of his skull.

JOOKS
Oh no. Oh fuck. Oh no. You weren't supposed to hear that.

LYDIA
One moment you're meeting the Queen then you're talking like the girl in The Exorcist when her head starts spinning round. What about that train crash?

JOOKS
Train crash. Oh my days. Question is, was there a train crash?

LYDIA
There definitely was a train crash. Checks out on the plane's wi-fi.

JOOKS
I was only a kid. Didn't know what I was doing. We just wanted to see what it would be like if a train crashed. Oh Lord, why hast thou forsaken me?

LYDIA
Hey JK, calm down, don't cry. Don't twist up your knickers. This is what happens when you rake up your nightmares. Just because there was a train crash doesn't mean it's what you're thinking. Think about it, how can an eight year old cause a train crash? Trains used to crash all the time back then. For all sorts of reasons.

JOOKS
Calm down? You think I can stay calm if I was involved? It's over. My career. My life. When the papers get hold of this.

LYDIA
When you say involved, has that been established? Never mind, no need to get into it, let's leave it. It'll blow over.

JOOKS
No it won't. We're talking a train crash for crying out loud.
That is major. Train crashes don't 'blow over'. People die.

LYDIA
Forty-nine.

JOOKS
Forty-nine. Dead?

LYDIA
Yes.

JOOKS
Oh my god. Oh my god. Forty-nine dead. Are you sure?

LYDIA
I looked it up. From the information I got from your sleep
talk (I was taking notes). Forty-nine dead and seventy
seriously injured. Let bygones be bygones. It could have
been so much worse.

JOOKS
I can't believe I revealed all this in my sleep. I thought I
had successfully rubbed it from memory.

LYDIA
You talked about dragging a tree trunk onto the tracks.

JOOKS
Rings a bell.

LYDIA
An eight year old? You want to do something about your
imagination, mate, it's running riot.

JOOKS
Forty-nine dead. They'll lock me up forever. I'll be the
most hated man in the country.

LYDIA
Yeah, you will be. If you keep telling everyone about it. You were eight years old for crying out loud, going to school on Black Boy Lane. You didn't stand a chance in those days. Anyone can understand that. You were a victim of your circumstances. What I can't believe is that the kid was called Threepenny Bit Tanner. Are you having a laugh? Did he have a twin?

JOOKS
I won't be able to live with myself if I don't confess.

LYDIA
Whoa, whoa, whoa. what is this mumbo-jumbo? You're talking like a pussy with an MBE. The train crash I'm talking about was in south London. Hallelujah. Harringay is in north.

JOOKS
What does it matter? A train crash is a train crash.

LYDIA
There wasn't a train crash in north London.

JOOKS
Then why am I crying over it?

LYDIA
The crash was twenty miles away in south London. How the fuck I know? Do I look like my name is Sigmund?

JOOKS
Are you sure?

LYDIA
Positive. Hundred percent. Checked and double checked. There were forty-four train crashes in the UK in the 1960s. I'm telling you, it was carnage out there. Six crashes in '65. Six crashes in '67. Six crashes in '68. Those days were like the apocalypse for train passengers. And not just from

acts of God. You had train drivers dozing off at the wheel, signalmen who didn't know their arses from their elbows, but more importantly their right from their left and on one occasion set fire to a locked carriage with passengers in. I mean, you couldn't make it up.

JOOKS

Well, in that case, if you're sure. What a relief. Now I can begin to enjoy this trip. Look down there. What an amazing landscape. It's not what you expect when you think of the desert. A mountain range. I thought it would be all Lawrence of Arabia. It looks amazing from up here but I wouldn't want the plane to go down now. By the time the rescuers come, survivors will be eating one another for tea.

LYDIA

And let me get this straight, who was fucking who up the arse?

JOOKS

Nobody. It was just a dream. A really bad dream. You were fucking me, I was fucking you, everybody was fucking everybody, but not literally. We were all shafting each other. On a positive note, we are so lucky to be in this game. I mean, I've been on some jollies in my time, but not one like this. First class to and fro. All expenses paid. Daily allowance. Five star hotel with a personal valet and a chauffeur with a Bentley to drive us everywhere. I would never have even considered visiting the land of the Arabian nights if it wasn't for this World Cup. As far as I am concerned it's a feudal system stuck in the medieval times. The way they murdered that bloke, what's his name, in their embassy in New York for instance, well, would you go to a country that would murder a man in cold blood? And then chop him up and dispose of him. In the embassy. I wouldn't. If it wasn't for the World Cup. Can you frigging believe it? And by all accounts nothing happens in this kingdom without a nod and a wink from His Majesty.

LYDIA

I'm not defending it but we're in the clear. Everybody else

is out here. The BBC, ITV, CNN. We've got to be out here too. Whether we like it or not. The World Cup for fucksake. This is a global story, mate. A World Cup in a country that stones you for shagging your neighbour's missus and flogs you for getting stoned. Mad, I know, but this could end up being the story of a lifetime. When the stars are aligned so perfectly and the sky is smiling you can't afford to miss the moment. We're journalists so we each have to justify it in our own way but we don't each have to live with ourselves.

JOOKS
A man was murdered in their embassy by embassy staff. I don't see how we can get around that by pretending it didn't happen.

LYDIA
Fucksake. Money talks, mate, money talks. It's all about the moollah in the land of the mullah. If you throw enough cash at it, and you raise the game, people will come.

JOOKS
Root of all evil.

LYDIA
We knew this was coming, though, didn't we? After Qatar did you honestly think that FIFA was going to turn down a truckload of cash from the land of the Arabian nights and a promise by the kingdom to give women equal rights and justice? No way José. I can't defend it but at the same time I can't attack it, so my thoughts on it will probably end up as a penalty shootout. Anyway, tighten your seatbelt. We're about to land.

Welcome to Scheherazade International. The home of the World Cup. It's 44 degrees out there so make sure you stay in the shade and if you're here for the football world championships do observe local rules. Absolutely no boozing. No Swearing. No sunbathing. And one more thing, no dissing the royal family like we do back in the UK. On behalf of B.O.O.C Airways and all the crew on board, have a lovely trip and we look forward to travelling with you again.

LYDIA
I can't believe what I just heard. Can you?

JOOKS
I've got an eerie feeling in my stomach.

LYDIA
No boozing? I'd like to see them enforce that if Arabianightsland beat England in that opening match.

JOOKS
I'm beginning to feel like I wish I wasn't on this trip. They don't tell you the 'don't diss the royal family like we do back home' bit in the brochures. I'm starting to shit myself.

LYDIA
Shh. Watch the language. You trying to get us killed? No swearing, remember? Tell you what, the footie is going to have to be out of this world to make this trip worthwhile, eh?

ALADDIN
Welcome to Arabianknightsland. Passport. Mr Kamiolakami-oluwalajoko. Born in Lagos. Journalist. Purpose of a visit – the World Cup. Duration of visit – two weeks. And... excuse me... there seems to be a problem. Please be patient... Ah, it is working again. Let me see now. Oh, I see. Mr Kamiolakamioluwalajoko. I see. Please. Come this way. My two colleagues will escort you. Come, follow me. Is this gentleman with you?

JOOKS
That's no gentleman. Lydia do you want to tell this bloke who I am and how big I am back home.

LYDIA
Never seen this bloke before in my life.

JOOKS
What Lydia... Lydia... what's going on? Lydia... are you having a laugh? We've worked together for nearly thirty

years.

LYDIA
No, just grinning. You know me, the woman with the golden grin. But I'm only thirty-three.

ALADDIN
Come this way, Mr Kamiolakamioluwalajoko. Please. Be my guest. I have a few questions to ask you.

JOOKS
What's going on? Is this how you treat your guests? Why have you detained me at the airport on entering your country? Do you realise who I am? I want your name, rank and number. I will be informing His Majesty's representatives at the British embassy. You're going to regret the day... wait, this is a very small room, why has it got brooms and buckets?

ALADDIN
Mr Kamiolakamioluwalajoko, please take a seat. I can answer all your questions. But first, do you recognise this article that you wrote a couple of years ago, disrespecting our king? Accusing him of the most heinous of crimes.

JOOKS
Oh, uhm, I don't recognise that article. I didn't write it. I can see why you think I wrote it, it's got my name on it.

ALADDIN
Yes, it has your name here at the bottom, look, and a picture of you also. There can be no mistake.

JOOKS
Yeah, a lot of people make the same mistake. It's an easy one to make. You see we share the same name but that's where the similarity ends. I am a totally different person from that JOOKS. You see, existentialistically I am not the same person I used to be. We don't stay the same do we? I

mean, you're not the same kid you used to be are you?

ALADDIN
But this was just a couple of years ago.

JOOKS
My point exactly. A couple of years ago I was an idiot. I was lost but now I'm found. I was blind. I couldn't see. But now that the rain has gone I'm an innocent man. So please release me let me go.

ALADDIN
I am extremely sorry, Mr JOOKS, Arabiankinightsland is un-democratically feudal. Impugning the good name of the king is a death wish. We are a civilised country so justice will be swift for the sword is mightier than the pen.

JOOKS
But I never said them things. Some bastard's trying to de-stroy me. It won't happen again, I swear.

ALADDIN
If you say so. What about this? Do you recognise this voice?

'I would never have even considered visiting the land of the Arabian nights if it wasn't for this World Cup. As far as I am concerned it's a feudal system stuck in the medieval times. The way they murdered that bloke, what's his name, in their embassy in New York. Well, would you go to a country that would murder a man in cold blood like that? And then chop him up and dispose of him. In the embassy. I wouldn't. If it wasn't for the World Cup... By all accounts nothing happens here without a nod and a wink...'

JOOKS
Oh fuck.

ALADDIN
Indeed Mr Kamiolakamioluwalajoko. Oh fuck.

EFFRIES

JOOKS
Where the fuck did you get that?

ALADDIN
What the fuck does it matter Mr Kamiolakamioluwalajoko?

JOOKS
What can I say? I apologise. I truly do. I didn't mean to hurt anyone or your great nation. It was a private conversation, On a plane. Not meant for your consumption. I apologise.I now realise the error of my ways. I am sorry.

WE'LL GO NO MORE A-RAVING
LATE INTO THE NIGHT
THOUGH THE HEART BE STILL AS LOVING
AND THE MOON BE STILL AS BRIGHT
FOR THE SWORD OUTWEARS ITS SHEATH
AND THE SOUL WEARS OUT THE BREAST
AND THE HEART MUST PAUSE TO BREATHE
AND LOVE ITSELF HAVE REST
THOUGH THE NIGHT WAS MADE FOR LOVING
AND THE DAY RETURNS TOO SOON
YET WE'LL GO NO MORE A-RAVING
BY THE LIGHT OF THE SILVERY MOON.

THE END... nearly.

EVERYTHING IS EVERYTHING

Yaow, mi idren, ah you dat?

YES, BELOVED, THIS IS ME. AND OH, BY THE WAY, I DON'T TALK LIKE THAT NO MORE. I'M NO LONGER A RASTAMAN. CALL ME ALHAJI.

Never mind that, fancy meeting you here. After all this time. And you're looking good, like the sun always shines. The good times keep rolling for you, yeah?

SEE THE SIGHT OF YOU. YOU'RE A SHADOW, A WANDERING CORPSE. TAKE A LOOK AT YOU. ABSOLUTE MESS. DON'T YOU HAVE ANY PRIDE IN YOURSELF? ISN'T THERE A MIRROR IN HERE? AND WHY ARE YOU LOOKING AT ME LIKE I'M THE UGLIEST THING IN THE WORLD?

Oh sorry, that's just my prickface. Got the fright of my life when I saw you. You know I ain't had much sleep and for a moment I thought your face looked like the face of my nightmares.

THE EXPRESSION ON YOUR BOAT, LIKE THIS AIN'T REALLY HAPPENING AND YOU MUST BE DREAMING. LIKE NIGHTS LIKE THIS DON'T COME ROUND EVERY DAY. THAT'S ONE WAY OF LOOKING AT IT.

Where am I, mate? One moment I was in that impenetrable vault and then the next moment, I'm on a plane to Arabianightsland. And then I arrive here and realise I've been spelling it wrong all this time. Their nights are spelt with a 'k'. Then they put me in this hole. I've been here for one thousand and one winks now and still no sign of the British ambassador. Can you tell me why I'm here? How did I get myself in this mess? Lydia stabs me in the back with some pussy boy move like I'm some piece of shit. What a pussyhole. How you going to leave man for dead like that? I'm not the kind of man who would punch a woman in the face but I'm not me anymore.

EFFRIES

FUCK THAT TALK, BELOVED. EXISTENTIALISM IS A HUMANISM. YOU HAVE RUN OUT OF LUCK. THAT'S SOME FUCKRIES. HOW COULD YOU NOT KNOW YOU WERE ON THE HIGHWAY TO HELL WHEN YOU PUT YOUR NAME TO THAT SUICIDE NOTE?

Suicide? Will it hurt?

YES, OF COURSE IT WILL. BUT ONLY FOR A NANOSECOND. THEN, LIKE A HEADLESS CHICKEN YOU WON'T FEEL A THING.

Oh, I love the way you say that. Headless chicken. That is so funny. You're a great actor. I'll give you that. And you've got some great lines. Honestly, you're coming across like you've done this loads of times.

YOU READY FOR THE STROKE OF TWELVE? ONE STROKE IS ALL WE NEED. HERE, TRY SOME OF THIS MARLEY WEED. IT WILL CALM YOU DOWN. TAKE YOUR MIND OFF. AND HERE, HAVE A DRINK. AND FOR THE LOVE OF GOD, FOR PITY'S SAKE, FOR YOUR FAMILY, FOR THE COMMUNITY AND FOR THE REST OF MANKIND, TAKE OFF THOSE SUNGLASSES. YOU'VE GOT NOTHING TO HIDE.

Cheers, thanks for the drink. I'm parched. This sitting around waiting for the final act is thirsty work. Forgive my manners, I'm drinking this down all at once... Aaaaaah! Yes. Delicious. Are you sure there weren't no alcohol in that cos I don't want to get in any trouble. I don't want to disrespect your country. The last thing I would do is transgress the strict ban on alcohol, even though I know that some of those foreigners are off their heads on booze in their apartments and hotel rooms. That's what I've heard. It's just that I'm getting that same buzz you get from Messrs Wray & Nephew if you know what I mean.

LET'S JUST SAY, BETWEEN YOU AND ME, SOMETHING TO CALM YOU DOWN AND SOMETHING TO GIVE YOU A BUZZ. IT MAKES MY JOB EASIER.

EFFRIES

You know, as we get closer to midnight, I can't believe that I used to believe in that load of bollocks about freedom and choice being the building blocks of the human condition. What a load of building bollocks. Life is all about the circumstances and the environment you are born into and live through, not the decisions you make. I realise that now. None of us is guilty of anything. We're all innocent. See what I mean? If I hadn't gone to school on Black Boy Lane think how differently my life would have turned out. Life's a lottery. It's different from man to man but those who are supposed to hit the jackpot hit the jackpot. Otherwise what's the point. What's the point of all the troubles we've seen if we can't keep dreaming that if it's meant to be it's meant to be our winning numbers? That's the fundamental problem with keeping me under arrest, as I see it. It's like my old man, he's a scientist through and through and through. Or was. He's not with us anymore. Sadly. Very sadly. But he didn't believe in anything that wasn't mathematically provable. Except... except for the existence of God. It don't make no sense. I know it's crazy asking this in a highly religious country but is it possible to believe in God and science?

IT'S TIME. COME. LET'S WALK. IT'S NEARLY MIDNIGHT.

Oh, is there one more scene? I didn't realise. God and science would be a nice way to end it though. Who wrote this screenplay anyway? How come you get all the best lines and I get all the shit ones? That's not right. I'm the matinee idol. Am I not supposed to be the star of the show? I thought you only had a bit-part. Walk where?

NEVER YOU MIND. DON'T EVEN THINK ABOUT IT. RASHID AND HAKIM WANT TO HOLD YOUR HANDS.

Shit, Hakim, that hurt. No need to shove me for real with your rifle butt. This is a movie, for eff's sake. I'm not really a dead man walking. Remember, we're acting. We're all actors. What I'm trying to say is, I grew up on the streets and when I think back to those times I can't

184

believe how there wasn't no child protection back then. We were thrown to the wolves every day at school and the streets. Don't get me wrong, I love the streets but they ate us kids alive for breakfast. We didn't stand a chance. And even though I have said 'no excuses' all my life I now get it. We've all got excuses. Like I said, nothing is our fault. It's the circumstances. That's what screws you up. For example, I took my girls to the ends the other day, to show them what's what so that they can know the streets and see where their dad is coming from, and we sat in the car right on Vale Terrace and just as I'm telling them about how we used to live in the two rooms downstairs part of the house and how we used to play football and cricket on the road and all that, Ellie suddenly pipes up:

Oh my gosh, is that a dead cat lying there on the pavement?

Sure enough it is. Amidst all the rubbish right outside our old front gate. That's just how it is in the ends. At least that's how it used to be. Full of dead cats. In those days if a cat had too many kittens and you couldn't give them away you drowned them then you chucked them over the railway line. There were loads of dead kittens over there. This one time, when I was just EIGHT I found this dead girl. This dead baby girl. Over by the railway line at the bottom of Stanhope Gardens. I know who did it. This bank robber. I saw him. We all did. We saw him chuck the bag over the embankment and because he looked all suspicious we jumped over the fence to see what was in the bag. We guessed it was a bag full of banknotes. Me and Dino and Nick the Greek. We wish. Turns out to be the most horrible thing I've ever seen in my life. A dead baby. It's a secret. Don't tell no one. It was over by where all the blackberry bushes are, you know, where people chuck their old prams and rubbish. I thought it was just a doll and so did Nick The Greek. But it moved. I swear. That's how I knew. And then it didn't move no more. That's when we ran away and swore not to tell anyone or to talk about it ever again. Imagine what having to keep a secret like that for the rest of your life does to a little kid.

ARE YOU SUGGESTING THAT THE INVISIBLE HAND OF

EFFRIES

ALLAH, THE MAGNIFICENT, TOOK THE LIFE OF A NEW-BORN BABY JUST SO THAT YOU COULD GET AWAY WITH DISSING HIS ROYAL HIGHNESS? HOW VERY UNFORTUNATE FOR THE OUTCOME OF THIS WHOLE SAGA.

You tell it like I'm the villain. I tell it like I'm the saint.

YOU SMELL LIKE YOU'VE JUST SHIT YOURSELF. OH, YOU HAVE. NO GREASEPAINT?

Oh my, this daylight. I forgot what it was like to see the sky.

THIS IS THE POINT WHERE YOUR STRENGTH DRAINS AWAY. I READ THE ORDER AND THEN, WHEN I GET A SIGNAL, I DO MY 'HAND OF GOD' THING. DON'T BLINK OR YOU'LL MISS IT.

Wait. Stop the acting for a moment. You're very good, by the way. Very convincing. That's why I shat myself. But where are we? What is this huge square you've taken me to? And who are all these people? Are they extras? It's like they're spectators. This is like being on TV. It's like they're expecting some kind of performance.

YOU'RE THE MAIN ATTRACTION. THE MATINEE IDOL. FOR REAL?

Oh my, is that the king behind them Ray-Bans? What's he doing here? And is that Lydia sitting next to him. Yoo-hoo, Lydia, it's me, Jooksy. Can you tell the king to send down that pardon pronto because I don't think these guys have got Equity cards.

JUSTICE/HUMILITY/TRUTH. BACK TOGETHER AGAIN.

And, oh my god, that long sword, gleaming by the light of the silvery moon. That doesn't look like a prop to me.

EFFRIES
LAST TWIST OF THE SWORD

I'VE NEVER SEEN SO MUCH SHIT. IT WAS EVERYWHERE. AND, HONESTLY, THE WHIFF OF IT. THE HARD STUFF IS BAD ENOUGH BUT THE RUNNY STUFF... SOMETHING TO BEHOLD. LIKE MY SWORD (I CALL IT SALADIN). IT RELAXS THE BOWELS. THE VERY SIGHT OF IT PUTS THE SHITS UP PEOPLE. FOR ONE THING, LOOK AT THE SIZE OF IT. IT'S NEARLY TWO METRES LONG. EVEN THE PROPHET WOULD HAVE STRUGGLED TO LIFT IT, LET ALONE SWING IT. BUT IT DOES THE JOB. EXCELLENTLY. IT'S MORE LIKE A SCALPEL WHEN IT COMES TO SPLITTING THE EDGE OF A SIXPENCE. AND IT'S OVER A THOUSAND YEARS OLD, FROM WHAT I'M TOLD. IT DON'T LOOK A DAY OLDER THAN BRAND NEW, WHICH MAKES IT LOOK LIKE A REPLICA. YOU KNOW WHAT AI'S LIKE. IT WILL TAKE OVER THIS JOB. OH, HEADS WILL ALWAYS ROLL, I CAN ASSURE YOU OF THAT. THAT'S THE HUMAN CONDITION. BUT WHAT CAN'T A ROBOT DO BETTER THAN A HUMAN? LISTEN, DON'T GET ME WRONG, I'M A BORN-AGAIN EXISTENTIALIST, REMEMBER? IF ROBOTS TAKE OVER, IT'S BECAUSE WE LET THEM TAKE OVER. IT'S OUR OWN FAULT. GOD AIN'T GOT NOTHING TO DO WITH IT. ROBOTS WEREN'T EVEN AROUND IN HIS DAY. I CAN'T COMPLAIN. I'VE HAD A GOOD INNINGS. AND SWINGINGS. I SLEEP EASY. IT DOES NOT KEEP ME AWAKE. I SEE MYSELF AS AN ARTIST DOING A GOOD JOB. I'VE HAD NO COMPLAINTS. NOT EVEN FROM JOOKS. KICKING AND SCREAMING AND SPITTING, WE EVENTUALLY MANAGED TO BLINDFOLD HIM AND SECURE HIM IN THE KNEELING POSITION TO MEET HIS MAKER. HE HOWLED LIKE A WOLF AND BARKED LIKE A DOG. AND SCREAMED AND SCREAMED AND CALLED ME ALL SORTS OF OFFENSIVE NAMES LIKE 'GOOGOO-DOOGOO DOOGOO-GOOGOO'. AND THEN THE CLOCK STRUCK MIDNIGHT AND HIS VERY LAST WORDS WERE *'FUCK Y−'*.

THINKING A HEAD

-OU. You hear me? FUCK YOU. I'll be waiting for you at the gates of hell, MOTHERFUCK-

Oh fuck, is that the rest of me running around like a headless torso? Oh shit, I'm not dead. Shit, all that blood. Fuck, I run fast without my head, without eyes to see. Story of my life.

Still alive? How come? That frigging priest and his sword. He only swung it once but it did the job. Sliced through my larynx like a block of margerine. Off with my head. A one cut decap. I can't speak. I can't move. My bloody head is stuck to the ground. I can't feel no pain. Only an itch I can't scratch but I'm alive. Don't ask me how. My mind is still turning. My brain is bursting. I've lost my torso and I'm at my wit's end. I think therefore I am but I think I'm better off dead. No arms, no legs, no arsehole and with only half a neck. A thinking head. That's not living. That's shit. *Je pense donc je suis* I am better dead than *merde*. And anyway, how long can a head survive without a body? One, two, three minutes? Hours, days, weeks, months? Years even? I cannot imagine anything worse than having to remain in this perpetual state of head for the rest of my natural life – not moving, not talking, not even blinking, just a head staring ahead. That ain't me so I may as well end it. But how? How is a head supposed to top itself when it can't walk and talk? Unless... unless I don't think. *Je pense pas donc je suis pas.* All I've got to do to kill myself is to stop thinking. Simple. Hallelujah. God is great. Allah akbar. It won't be long now, it's only a matter of time now, if I think hard enough I'm bound to stop thinking and then it's goodbye cruel world as far as I'm concerned. Easy.

Oh for fuck sake, that's all I need, a sandstorm in my face and... here come the ants. I see the king's not hanging around. His keffiyeh's round his face and it's like he and his entourage can't wait to get out of here. And, fuck, that really is Lydia beside him. Can you believe it?

I don't know what to believe anymore. Once your belief is shaken everything else is wobbly. How can she be cosying up with His Majesty like that? That's what is making me think that I've been set-up and that she's been the one behind it all this time. I might just be saying that because I've been beheaded and, as you might expect, that is affecting my critical thinking, fair enough, but if it wasn't for her eagerness I wouldn't be here. I trust her... I trusted her. She sorted out the visas. She was the one who got the accreditation and she made it sound sweet like we were all going to get a Fabergé egg each in our goodie bags just for being here to cover the World Cup. When she realised I couldn't be bought with an omelette she got the kingdom to throw in equal rights for women bikers and, well, I couldn't say no could I? You know what I'm like with motorcycles.

And now she's getting off with the king. I don't believe it. I say 'she' but who knows. I'm not sure about anything to do with Lydia anymore. Is the king aware of pronoun protocol? Or am I just being vindictive and prejudiced now? I can't lie, I've got the hump about the way she abandoned me at the airport and sold me down the river by saying she had never seen me before in her life? I can't get that betrayal out of my mind. It's brought out the male chauvinist pig in me. Not to talk of the institutional racism.

But then who can I trust? Certainly not that frigging priest with all that 'bringing the years of my life together on a zoom call' business.

I must have been off my head to believe I wasn't dreaming. What a load of bollocks. Can you believe I actually believed he could do that? He had me talking myself to sleep for hours and believing that I was talking to myself in my sleep and you know what that's like, you're bound to say anything in your dreams, you're bound to admit to anything, you're bound to confess to things you don't know nothing about. You're talking complete bollocks. For England. One big confessional. But it never happened. None of it. And if it never happened, nothing happened. And then he pulls that big sword out of its massive shaft and I saw (swear to god) the same glint in his eye as I saw in Johnny Wanker's eye when he was salivating at the prospect of perforating Plop-Plops from behind. A dead ringer. I'll suck your dick if the priest is not a Wanker.

EFFRIES

More importantly I've worked out who this has been about all along, who tried to run me down, who it was who tried to shoot me and promised to duppy me by midnight. I worked it out. Cos I didn't put my name to that Ariabianknightsland article. Guess who got a job as a sub-editor at the publisher at the same time? Yes. That's right. You know... erm... you know, gosh, old wotsit, I can't think–

...FOR NOW